Neurosteroids and Brain Function

Fidia Research Foundation Symposium Series
Volume 8

Fidia Research Foundation Symposium Series

Neurosteroids and Brain Function

Fidia Research Foundation Symposium Series
Volume 8

Editors

Erminio Costa, M.D.
Fidia-Georgetown Institute for the Neurosciences
Georgetown University School of Medicine
Washington, D.C.

Steven M. Paul, M.D.
National Institute of Mental Health
National Institutes of Health
Bethesda, Maryland

1991
Thieme Medical Publishers, Inc. NEW YORK
Georg Thieme Verlag STUTTGART • NEW YORK

Thieme Medical Publishers, Inc.
381 Park Avenue South
New York, New York 10016

Library of Congress Cataloging-in-Publication Data

Neurosteroids and brain function / editor, Erminio Costa.
  p. cm. -- (Fidia Research Foundation symposium series : v. 8)
  Based on a conference held Nov. 11, 1991 in St. Louis, Mo.
  Includes bibliographical references and index.
  ISBN 0-86577-422-6. -- ISBN 3-13-776201-4
  1. Neuroendocrinology--Congresses. 2. Steroid hormones-
-Congresses. 3. Steroid hormones--Receptors--Congresses.
 4. Adrenocortical hormones--Congresses. 5. Adrenocortical
hormones-Receptors--Congresses. 6. Brain--Congresses.
 I. Costa, Erminio II. Series.
  (DNLM: 1. Brain--physiology--congresses. 2. Receptors, Steroid-
-metabolism--congresses. 3. Steroids--metabolism--congresses. W1
FI321F v. 9 / QU 85 N4945 1991)
QP356.4.N5 1992
612.8'22--dc20
DNLM/DLC
for Library of Congress
                                             91-5137
                                                CIP

Important Note: Medicine is an ever-changing science. Research and clinical experience are continually broadening our knowledge, in particular our knowledge of proper treatment and drug therapy. Insofar as this book mentions any dosage or application, readers may rest assured that the authors, editor and publishers have made every effort to ensure that such references are strictly in accordance with the state of knowledge at the time of production of the book. Nevertheless, every user is requested to examine carefully the manufacturers' leaflets accompanying each drug to check on his or her own responsibility whether the dosage schedules recommended therein or the contraindications stated by the manufacturers differ from the statements made in the present book. Such examination is particularly important with drugs that are either rarely used or have been newly released on the market.

Some of the product names, patents and registered designs referred to in this book are in fact registered trademarks or proprietary names even though specific reference to this fact is not always made in the text. Therefore, the appearance of a name without designation as proprietary is not to be construed as a representation by the publisher that it is in the public domain.

Printed in the United States of America

5 4 3 2 1

TMP ISBN 0-86577-422-6
GTV ISBN 3-13-776201-4

Preface

Steroids have pleiotropic effects on the CNS, where they subserve a number of neuroendocrine and behavioral functions. Many of these effects appear to be mediated via classical intracellular steroid receptors which modify transcriptionally directed changes in protein synthesis. Such genomic mechanisms underlie the ability of steroid hormones to alter the expression of important genes in the brain and pituitary, including those involved in modifying the activity of the hypothalamic-pituitary-adrenal axis (HPA) (e.g., hypothalamic peptide-releasing factors, pituitary hormones) and those for neurotrophic factors such as nerve growth factor. Cytoplasmic steroid receptors within discrete regions of the CNS are important in mediating the negative feedback of glucocorticoids on HPA function, and appear to mediate the stress-related death of hippocampal neurons. The latter is a phenomenon possibly related to neuronal loss observed during the aging process.

In addition to their well-described genomic effects, some steroids have long been recognized to alter the excitability of the CNS rapidly. More than 50 years ago, H. Selye first reported the sedative/anesthetic effects of progesterone and deoxycorticosterone, and demonstrated that their natural A-ring reduced metabolites are potent hypnotic agents. This observation led to a number of more recent studies which demonstrate that various natural and synthetic 3α-hydroxy ring-A reduced pregnanes—including the steroid anesthetic 3α-hydroxy-5α-pregnane-11,20-dione (alphaxalone) and the natural metabolites 3α-hydroxy-5α-pregnan-20-one (allopregnanolone) and 3α,21-dihydroxy-5α-pregnan-20-one (allotetrahydroDOC)—directly interact with receptors for the major inhibitory neurotransmitter in the brain, γ-aminobutyric acid (GABA). Both electrophysiological and biochemical studies have shown that these neuroactive steroids are relatively high-affinity ligands of central and peripheral $GABA_A$ receptors, and can allosterically augment $GABA_A$ receptor–mediated Cl^- ion conductance in a manner similar to that of the anesthetic barbiturates. Other steroids, including the synthetic amidine steroid 3α-hydroxy-16-imino-5β,17-azaandrostan-11-one (RU 5135), as well as the natural sulfate esters of pregnenolone and dehydroepiandrosterone, have been shown to antagonize $GABA_A$ receptor–mediated Cl^- ion conductance. Thus, steroids can have both "agonist" and "antagonist" actions at central $GABA_A$ receptors, resulting in augmentation or inhibition of inhibitory synaptic events, respectively. The physiological significance of these findings is supported by recent experiments which show that the levels of these neuroactive 3α-hydroxysteroids (allopregnanolone and allotetrahydroDOC) in the blood and brain fluctuate during a variety of physiological states (e.g., stress, estrus/menses, pregnancy). In some cases the blood and brain levels of these steroids appear sufficient to modulate $GABA_A$ receptors. Thus, 3α-hydroxysteroids may function as endogenous ligands or modulators of $GABA_A$ receptors.

In 1981, E.-E. Baulieu coined the term *neurosteroid* to designate a steroid hormone intermediate, dehydroepiandrosterone sulfate, which can be measured in the brain at concentrations independent of the known peripheral sources of these steroids, such as the adrenal glands or gonads. The de novo formation of neurosteroids such as dehydro-epiandrosterone and pregnenolone has been demonstrated to occur in the mammalian brain via the classical mevalonate pathway to cholesterol, followed by cytochrome P-450–catalyzed side-chain cleavage of choles-terol to pregnenolone. Now, glia (and perhaps neurons) appear capable of synthesizing neurosteroids, and can further oxidize pregnenolone to progesterone. The subsequent reduction of progesterone to allopreg-nanolone via 5α-reductase activity has been demonstrated in mixed primary cultures of neurons and glia.

Recently, the peripheral benzodiazepine receptor, located on the outer mitochondrial membrane (and enriched in adrenal mitochon-dria), has been shown possibly to play an important role in both adreno-corticotropic hormone–induced steroidogenesis in the adrenal, as well as in the synthesis of steroids by glia. Collectively, these data suggest that neurosteroids synthesized in the brain modify a variety of CNS functions via "nonclassical" steroid receptors, which in some cases are associated with receptors for both inhibitory and excitatory neurotransmitters.

Finally, these novel steroid recognition sites may represent important targets for the development of drugs for a variety of neurological and psychiatric disorders. A dissociation of the glucocorticoid and neuro-protectant actions of steroids, for example, resulted in the discovery of a series of synthetic 21-aminosteroids, which may prove useful for treating brain injury induced by ischemia or trauma.

This volume on Neurosteroids and Brain Function explores the mechanisms responsible for the actions of steroids on various aspects of brain and neuroendocrine function, and covers the role of "classical" steroid receptors as well as the role of the more recently described membrane-bound steroid recognition sites. Evidence supporting the de novo synthesis of steroids by the brain (i.e., the biosynthesis of neuro-steroids) is reviewed and discussed in light of newer findings on the rapid modulatory actions of steroids on both inhibitory and excitatory synaptic events.

Erminio Costa, M.D.
Steven M. Paul, M.D.

Contents

I
Steroid Receptors and Brain Function

II
Steroid Regulation and Brain Function

III
Plenary Lecture

IV
Neurosteroids

V
Recent Studies on the Regulation of
Steroid Synthesis in the Brain and Periphery

I

Steroid Receptors and Brain Function

Mineralo- and Glucocorticoid Receptor Balance and Homeostatic Control

*E. Ronald de Kloet, Ph.D., and *Marian Joëls, Ph.D.*

*Division of Medical Pharmacology, Center for Bio-Pharmaceutical Sciences, University of Leiden, 2300 RA Leiden, The Netherlands; and *Department of Experimental Zoology, University of Amsterdam, Kruislaan 320, 1098 SM Amsterdam, The Netherlands*

Steroids control brain function via different modes of action, which can be distinguished in terms of mechanism and time domain. In one mode of action, steroids affect gene expression by slow onset and long duration. These effects are exerted by the steroid hormones secreted from the peripheral endocrine glands. These hormones readily enter the brain and bind to intracellular receptors, causing genomic effects on cell metabolism and ion regulation. In another mode, steroids can have direct membrane effects, which occur within seconds and involve binding to receptor-gated ion channels. The latter actions, exerted by steroid hormone metabolites or neurosteroids generated in the brain, will not be discussed here.

This chapter focuses on gene-mediated corticosteroid effects in the brain. First, we will present a brief survey on brain corticosteroid receptor diversity and its implications for centrally regulated functions. Then, we will show a specific example of the cellular mechanism of corticosteroid action mediated by two intracellular receptor types in hippocampal neurons. Our contribution concludes with a new concept of the role of corticosteroid receptors in genomic control of cellular homeostasis.

Central Corticosteroid Receptor Diversity

The brain contains mineralocorticoid (MR) and glucocorticoid (GR) receptors. MRs have aldosterone-selective properties in periventricular

3

brain regions and corticosterone-selective properties elsewhere, notably in the neurons of the hippocampus. The steroid selectivity of MRs hinges on the activity of colocalized 11β-hydroxysteroid dehydrogenase. GRs are widely distributed. The highest density of GRs occurs in neurons involved in organization of the stress response, such as the parvocellular paraventricular neurons, brainstem aminergic neurons and hippocampal neurons. In the latter, MRs and GRs are colocalized. MRs bind corticosterone—the naturally occurring ligand of the rat—with six- to tenfold higher affinity than that displayed by GRs, which results in differential activation of MRs and GRs as a function of the circulating corticosterone level (Figure 1A) (1,2).

In our studies on the role of these receptors in centrally regulated function, we examined the effect of the removal of the adrenals and subsequent replacement with receptor-specific agonists, and the application of selective steroid antagonists intracerebroventricularly or locally in the brain. Brain functions were analyzed based on criteria guided by the topography and binding properties of the receptor systems. These studies showed that the aldosterone-selective central MRs mediate long-term influences on central regulation of salt homeostasis and associated functions such as cardiovascular control (3). However, the corticosterone-selective MRs in the hippocampus appear to be involved in neuroendocrine regulation and behavior. Blockade of the hippocampal MRs with antimineralocorticoids suggests that via this receptor, corticosterone suppresses the basal activity and the sensitivity to stress of the hypothalamic-pituitary-adrenal (HPA) axis. Hippocampal GRs seem to mediate opposite effects of corticosterone from those exerted by MRs in neuroendocrine regulation. In the parvocellular paraventricular neurons and the pituitary corticotrophs, corticosterone blocks stress-induced activation of the HPA axis by GR-mediated negative feedback action, which probably

Figure 1. A: Cumulative occupancy of soluble MRs and GRs in the hippocampus 1 hr after subcutaneous (s.c.) administration of increasing doses of corticosterone to rats 24 hr after adrenalectomy. Occupancy calculated from labeling available MRs and GRs with radioligands in corticosterone-treated rats, subtracted from total number of sites (MR + GR) measured in untreated rats. Binding capacity based on Scatchard analysis. *Dotted area* represents MR occupancy. Full MR + GR occupancy = 100%. (Data reprinted in part from refs. 1 and 9, with permission.) **B**: Responses to 5HT of CA1 pyramidal neurons in slices from adrenalectomized rats **1**) before steroid treatment, **2**) after 20-min exposure to 3 nM aldosterone, or **3**) after perfusion of aldosterone with RU 28362. Numbers correspond to numbered arrows in **A**, representing conditions in which the MR is **1**) not occupied or **2**) mostly occupied, or **3**) in which the MR and GR are activated. *Downward deflections* represent voltage responses to constant current pulses. For correct estimation of 5HT-induced changes in resistance, membrane potential in **1** and **3** was temporarily brought to pretreatment level to compensate for rectifying properties of the membrane.

A

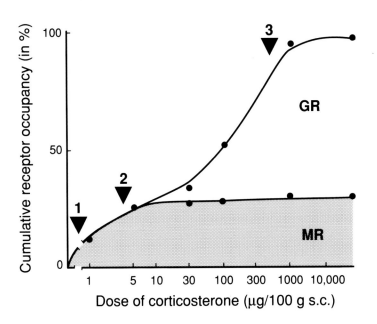

B

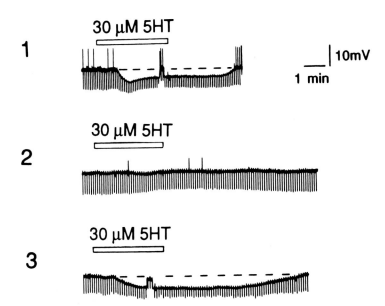

overrides the putative positive feedback signal from hippocampal GR activation. Accordingly, intraventricular administration of either gluco- or mineralocorticoid antagonist prolongs stress-induced HPA activation, but different mechanisms are involved. We propose that the anti-mineralocorticoid enhances stress responsiveness via the hippocampus, whereas the antiglucocorticoid interferes with glucocorticoid-negative feedback at the hypothalamic-pituitary level (4).

In behavior, central MR activation is involved in processes underlying evaluation of the situation and response selection, which was reflected in an altered search strategy in the Morris water maze. GR activation occurring with higher corticosterone levels facilitates storage of spatial information (5). Thus, corticosteroid effects mediated by MRs and GRs in behavior and neuroendocrine regulation can be clearly differentiated. In the next section we provide data on the cellular mechanism underlying corticosteroid action in the hippocampus.

Cellular Effects of Corticosteroids

Using electrophysiological recording techniques, we investigated how corticosteroid hormones at the cellular level can affect electrical activity of pyramidal neurons in the CA1 area of the hippocampus, which contain MRs and GRs (1). In general, the actions of the steroids developed with a delay of approximately 1 hr and were prevented in the presence of a protein synthesis inhibitor. This finding indicates that the corticosteroid actions we studied, in contrast with the actions of neurosteroids described so far, are mediated by the classical intracellular steroid receptors via a genomic mechanism of action. The specific aspects of these MR- and GR-mediated effects on electrical activity will be illustrated by the action of corticosteroids on serotonin (5HT)-induced responses in hippocampal neurons.

In CA1 pyramidal neurons, 5HT induces a hyperpolarization of the membrane and a decrease of the membrane resistance, via the $5HT_{1a}$ receptor (6). These effects result from a 5HT-evoked opening of K^+ channels. Brief application (20 min) of aldosterone (3 or 30 nM) in vitro markedly reduced both the 5HT-induced membrane hyperpolarization and resistance decrease of neurons recorded 1 to 4 hr after the steroid application (7) (Figure 1B). The action of aldosterone could be prevented by addition of the MR antagonist spironolactone. The mixed MR and GR agonist corticosterone (30 nM) reduced 5HT responses in some neurons but the overall change did not attain statistical significance.

However, when corticosterone was perfused with the GR antagonist RU 38486, 5HT responses again were largely suppressed. These data indicate that the suppressive effect of corticosteroid hormones on 5HT responses in the hippocampus is mediated by the MR.

In a follow-up study, the effect of aldosterone on 5HT responses did not occur when cycloheximide, a protein synthesis inhibitor, was added to the in vitro preparation (8). This observation and the fact that the steroid actions were observed with a delay of at least 1 hr support a genomic mechanism of action for MR agonists. It was next questioned which part of the cascade from the $5HT_{1a}$ receptor (via G protein) to the receptor-linked K^+ conductance might be the target for the MR-induced protein. With a membrane binding assay for the $5HT_{1a}$ receptor agonist 8-hydroxy-2-(di-n-propylamino)tetralin (8-OH-DPAT), neither the binding capacity nor the affinity of the $5HT_{1a}$ receptor appeared largely affected by MR ligands applied in vitro (7). Desensitization of the $5HT_{1a}$ receptor did not occur before or after steroid treatment. Finally, the response to baclofen, an agonist of the $GABA_B$ receptor which is linked via a G protein to the same K^+ conductance as the $5HT_{1a}$ receptor, was not appreciably changed after treatment of the preparation with aldosterone. However, 5HT responses in the same neurons were significantly reduced. Now, it is unclear how the MR-mediated action on 5HT responsiveness is accomplished. One possibility is that activation of the MR eventually changes the coupling of the $5HT_{1a}$ receptor to the G protein.

In contrast to MR agonists, GR ligands were not effective in reducing the 5HT response of CA1 pyramidal neurons. However, application of the GR agonist RU 28362 prevented the action of MR agonists on 5HT responsiveness (9) (Figure 1B). How GR activation can interfere with MR-mediated actions has not been resolved, but because of the large degree of homology in the GR- and MR-DNA binding domains, interaction between MRs and GRs may arise at the DNA level. The reversal of MR-mediated actions by GR occupation has important consequences for the effectiveness of the natural mixed MR and GR agonist corticosterone in reducing 5HT responses. This concept is exemplified by a series of experiments in which either low (0.5 nM, approximately the K_d for corticosterone binding to MRs at 0°C) or high (5 nM, K_d for binding to GRs) concentrations of corticosterone were continuously perfused. With 0.5 nM corticosterone, 5HT responses were initially similar to the control responses, but had a delay of approximately 2 hr. 5HT-induced membrane hyperpolarization was significantly suppressed. In contrast, 5 nM corticosterone resulted in a relatively fast (<2 hr) suppression of 5HT responses, but with a delay of approximately 2 hr the initial suppression was reversed and 5HT responses returned to control levels (9). This result indicates that the MR-mediated decrease of 5HT responses in the hippocampus may only occur under conditions of low adrenocortical activity or, on a long-term basis, if the balance between MRs and GRs is shifted in the direction of the MR.

The effects described in this chapter of corticosteroid hormones on 5HT responsiveness illustrate a principle that also has been observed for other actions of steroids on electrical activity. Thus, by reducing a 5HT-induced inhibitory effect, MR ligands potentially enhance the excitability in the CA1 area. The MR-mediated effect is reversed by GR ligands, which therefore suppresses hippocampal excitability. Similar actions by MR ligands, leading to an increase in excitability which then is reversed or opposed by GR-mediated effects, have been described for amino acid–mediated synaptic input (10), for noradrenergic responsiveness (11,12), and for cellular accommodation (13). Thus, the cellular effects of corticosteroids via coordinative MR- and GR-mediated actions may add to a mechanism by which the brain, over a period of hours, can control its cellular excitability. Whether cellular excitability is enhanced or attenuated by steroids critically depends on the balance in MR and GR occupation.

Conclusion

The data we have collected over the past years demonstrate that the central MR- and GR-mediated effects restore homeostasis and proceed in a coordinate manner, but are antagonistic. Accordingly, based on the studies in the hippocampus, a new concept has emerged in which a balance of MR- and GR-mediated responses is critical for the set point of homeostatic control (14). This hypothesis places Selye's "pendulum" hypothesis (15) of opposing mineralocorticoid and glucocorticoid actions in the perspective of colocalized MRs and GRs mediating the effect of one single adaptive hormone, corticosterone. Shifts in the MR/GR balance may alter susceptibility to stress and perhaps to stress-related brain diseases. Such shifts may occur during chronic hyper- or hyposecretion of adrenal corticosteroids.

Acknowledgment

This research is supported by NWO grants 900–546–092 (E.R.dK.) and 900–553–028 (M.J.). The supply of RU 38486 and RU 28362 by Roussel-

UCLAF is gratefully acknowledged. We thank Ellen M. Heidema for editorial assistance.

References

1. Reul JMHM, De Kloet ER. Two receptor systems for corticosterone in rat brain: microdistribution and differential occupation. *Endocrinology* 1985;117:2505–2512.
2. De Kloet ER, Reul JMHM. Feedback action and tonic influence of corticosteroids on brain functions: a concept arising from the heterogeneity of brain receptor systems. *Psychoneuroendocrinology* 1987;12:83–105.
3. Van den Berg DTWM, De Kloet ER, Van Dijken HH, et al. Differential central effects of mineralocorticoid and glucocorticoid agonists and antagonists on blood pressure. *Endocrinology* 1990;126:118–124.
4. Ratka A, Sutanto W, Bloemers M, et al. On the role of brain mineralocorticoid (Type I) and glucocorticoid (Type II) receptors in neuroendocrine regulation. *Neuroendocrinology* 1989;50:117–123.
5. Oitzl MS, De Kloet ER. Selective corticosteroid-antagonists modulate specific aspects of spatial learning. *Behav Neurosci* 1991;(in press).
6. Anwyl R. Neurophysiological actions of 5-hydroxytryptamine in the vertebrate nervous system. *Prog Neurobiol* 1990;35:451–468.
7. Joëls M, Hesen W, De Kloet ER. Mineralocorticoid hormones suppress serotonin-induced hyperpolarization of rat hippocampal CA1 neurons. *J Neurosci* 1991;(in press).
8. Karst H, Joëls M. The induction of corticosteroid actions on membrane properties of hippocampal CA1 neurons requires protein synthesis. *Neurosci Lett* 1991;(in press).
9. Joëls M, De Kloet ER. Coordinative mineralocorticoid- and glucocorticoid receptor-mediated control of responses to serotonin in rat hippocampus. *Neuroendocrinology* 1991;(in press).
10. Rey M, Carlier E, Soumireu-Mourat B. Effect of RU 486 on hippocampal slice electrophysiology in normal and ADX BALB/c mice. *Neuroendocrinology* 1989;49:120–125.
11. Joëls M, De Kloet ER. Effects of glucocorticoid and norepinephrine on the excitability in the hippocampus. *Science* 1989;245:1502–1505.
12. Joëls M, Bouma G, Hesen W, et al. Increased effect of noradrenaline on synaptic responses in rat CA1 hippocampal area after adrenalectomy. *Brain Res* 1991;550:347–352.
13. Joëls M, De Kloet ER. Mineralocorticoid receptor-mediated changes in membrane properties of rat CA1 pyramidal neurons in vitro. *Proc Natl Acad Sci USA* 1990;87:4495–4498.
14. De Kloet ER. Brain corticosteroid receptor balance and homeostatic control. *Front Neuroendocrinol* 1991;12:95–164.
15. Selye H. *Stress. The physiology and pathology of exposure to stress.* Montreal: Acta Medica, 1950.

Enzymes, Receptors and Steroid Specificity

John W. Funder, M.D., Ph.D.

Baker Medical Research Institute, Melbourne, Victoria 3181, Australia

This chapter focuses on adrenal steroids and their mechanism of action in two organs not commonly considered part of the brain—the kidney and the adrenal medulla. Despite this apparent distancing, I have chosen to review studies on these two organs to illustrate what we know, and our areas of current ignorance, about receptors for adrenal steroids. In addition, I will briefly canvass the ways in which these peripheral findings might be applied to the CNS.

The adrenal cortex is the unique source of two classes of steroid hormones—mineralocorticoids (aldosterone, from the lungfish up) and glucocorticoids (cortisol, or corticosterone in rats and mice). Both mineralocorticoid receptors (MRs) and glucocorticoid receptors (GRs) were distinguished almost 20 years ago and have subsequently been cloned and sequenced in a number of species. GRs have high affinity for potent synthetic steroids such as dexamethasone and triamcinolone acetonide, have reasonable affinity for cortisol and corticosterone, and have lower affinity for aldosterone. In contrast, MRs have equivalent affinity for aldosterone, deoxycorticosterone, corticosterone and (in the human) cortisol. Although high levels of MRs are found in classical Na-transporting epithelia (colon, kidney, parotid), even higher levels are found in the hippocampus—not normally considered a site of physiologic mineralocorticoid activity—and not inconsiderable levels are found elsewhere in the brain.

These findings pose two questions. Given that circulating levels of physiologic glucocorticoids are commonly two to three orders of magnitude higher than those of aldosterone, the first question is that of MR specificity in mineralocorticoid target tissues: how does aldosterone occupy such nonselective MRs in the face of much higher glucocorticoid levels? Second, if MRs—perhaps better termed Type I receptors—in the hippocampus respond to circulating levels of glucocorticoids, what are the implications of tissues and cells having both high-affinity (Type I receptors) and moderate-affinity (Type II, or classical GRs) receptors for glucocorticoid hormones?

Currently, there are limited answers to the first question, that of the mechanisms conferring aldosterone specificity on the intrinsically nonselective MRs. In brief, specificity appears to reflect the activity of at least two enzymes—18-methyloxidase in the adrenal gland, responsible for the C18 aldehyde group of aldosterone, and 11β-hydroxysteroid dehydrogenase (11-HSD) in mineralocorticoid target tissues. The latter enzyme converts cortisol and corticosterone to their receptor-inactive 11-dehydro metabolites (cortisone, 11-dehydrocorticosterone). Aldosterone is not similarly metabolized, reflecting the cyclization of the C11 hydroxyl with the C18 aldehyde group, and thus, formation of a protected 11,18 hemiketal configuration.

At present, a number of ongoing studies in this area concern the factors determining Type I receptor occupancy in various tissues:

(i) Marked species differences appear to exist in terms of 18-methyl-oxidase activity. For years, it was held that a single enzyme (11,18-hydroxylase) was responsible for 18-hydroxylation in the zona glomerulosa, and for 11β-hydroxylation in glomerulosa and in fasciculata. Recently, however, 18-hydroxylation in the rat, but not in the bovine, has been shown to reflect activity of a related but quite distinct gene from that coding for 11β-hydroxylase. In the human, equivalent specific 18-hydroxylation activity to date has been shown only in adenomata. Thus, the mechanisms of generating the cyclized and protected 11,18 hemiketal species appear to vary between species. The implications of such diversity remain to be explored.

(ii) The 11-HSD purified from rat liver by Carl Monder, and subsequently used for the generation of antiserum and the elucidation of cDNA sequence, is expressed in highest abundance in liver, testis, kidney and lung. Within the kidney it is expressed predominantly in proximal collecting tubules and in medullary interstitial cells, which are not sites of the antinatriuretic effect of aldosterone. Studies on steroid metabolism by cultured cortical collecting tubules, by dissected nephron segments or by kidney slices have shown colocalization of high levels of 11-HSD activity in physiologic mineralocorticoid target tissues with high levels of MRs. These studies appear to provide excellent evidence for the existence of a second species of 11-HSD (11-HSD2) distinct from that purified and cloned by Monder (11-HSD1) and responsible for conferring mineralocorticoid specificity on Type I receptors. The physiologic role of 11-HSD1, therefore, appears to be modulation of Type II, GR occupancy in classical glucocorticoid target tissues (such as liver or lung).

(iii) The role of 11-HSD2 appears to exclude not only glucocorticoids from Type I receptors in aldosterone target cells, but also glucocorticoids from GRs in these cells. Studies have been conducted on patients with pseudohypoaldosteronism (i.e., without MRs), on adrenalectomized rats given the selective glucocorticoid RU 28362 and on cultured cortical collecting tubules exposed to aldosterone, dexamethasone or RU 28362. These studies have shown that glucocorticoid occupancy of GRs in classical mineralocorticoid target tissues is followed by a classical mineralocorticoid response, in terms of Na and K fluxes. These studies suggest that the response element(s) responsible for MR regulation of gene expression may be similarly or identically activated by ligand-bound GRs, and emphasize the importance of prereceptor enzymatic mechanisms in protecting not merely Type I receptors, but the cell as a whole, from physiologic glucocorticoids.

(iv) Whereas 11-HSD appears to be an adequate mechanism to explain how glucocorticoids can be excluded from mineralocorticoid target cells, it cannot explain how progesterone and deoxycorticosterone, which commonly circulate at concentrations equal to or higher than those of aldosterone, can be excluded. In addition to 11-keto derivatives, rat kidneys perfused with tritiated corticosterone yield 20β-reduced metabolites of both corticosterone and 11-dehydrocorticosterone. The enzyme 3α,20β-HSD may thus exclude deoxycorticosterone and progesterone from Type I receptors, for which they have an equal (deoxycorticosterone) or approximately 20% (progesterone) affinity as they have for aldosterone. In addition, because both 11-dehydrogenated and 20β-reduced metabolites of glucocorticoids are receptor-inactive, and both 11-HSD and 3α,20β-HSD are carbenoxolone-inhibited, 11-HSD and 3α,20β-HSD may combine to render glucocorticoids receptor-inactive regardless of the state of oxidation or reduction of cofactors within the cell.

(v) Consistent with its putative role in modulating Type II receptor occupancy by glucocorticoids, 11-HSD1 has been shown immunohistochemically to be widely distributed in the brain, particularly in the hippocampus. In contrast with the kidney, 11-HSD1 has been colocalized in Type I receptor–containing cells in the hippocampus, as well as in glial cells. In addition, the hippocampal species of 11-HSD1 appears to show different substrate specificity, in that rat hippocampal preparations metabolize corticosterone but not cortisol. As yet there are no data on the existence or localization of 11-HSD2 in the brain, although from salt-appetite studies, aldosterone-selective Type I receptors (as well as high-affinity Type I GRs) clearly exist within the CNS. What also has yet to be established is the extent to which Type I and Type II receptor occupancy are yoked to mediate common effects over a broad band of steroid concentrations, to what extent they mediate different effects, and how 11-HSD1 modulates occupancy of either or both.

The second focus of this chapter does not concern the modulatory effect of enzymes on receptors for steroids, but rather receptors for steroids on enzyme activity. For years it has been accepted that the adrenal medullary enzyme phenyl-ethanolamine N-methyl transferase (PNMT), responsible for the final step in adrenaline biosynthesis, is glucocorticoid-responsive. Classically, enzyme activity falls after hypophysectomy and is restored by administered adrenocorticotropin hormone or greatly supraphysiologic doses of corticosterone or dexamethasone. More recently, the cDNA sequence for PNMT has been established and PNMT mRNA levels have been increased by glucocorticoids in a dose-dependent fashion via interaction with a classical glucocorticoid response element in the 5' untranslated region.

In a recent series of studies (1) on the in vivo action of administered glucocorticoids on PNMT mRNA levels and enzyme activity, we established that dexamethasone and RU 28362, given daily at semilogarithmic doses from 1 µg to 1 mg for 7 days, both progressively elevate adrenal medullary PNMT mRNA activity. The dose-response curve is similar for both steroids, with dexamethasone appearing approximately three times as potent as RU 28362, as is the case for their effects on thymus and adrenal weight. At the highest doses of steroid used, a 15- to 20-fold increase in the specific activity of PNMT mRNA is found on densitometry of Northern blots. In contrast, however, at low doses of both glucocorticoids (1 to 30 µg/day), a progressive fall in PNMT activity to levels approximately two-thirds those of basal is seen in the contralateral adrenal. At higher doses (100 to 1000 µg) of dexamethasone, PNMT activity progressively rises so that at the highest dose used, levels of PNMT activity equal those in rats given vehicle. In contrast, higher doses of RU 28362 are followed by plateau levels of PNMT activity, between 60% and 70% of basal.

We interpret these data as follows:

(i)   In vivo, PNMT mRNA levels are positively regulated by glucocorticoids, presumably via classical GRs, as reflected by the marked increase in mRNA levels with progressive doses of both steroids. Such an increase over basal suggests the effect may not be directly on the adrenal medulla, given that adrenal medullary levels of corticosterone in the basal state would be expected to saturate classical Type II GRs.

(ii) The dehiscence between the steroid-induced increase in PNMT mRNA and the pattern of PNMT activity in response to steroids suggests that factors other than PNMT abundance are rate limiting in terms of its activity. Such rate-limiting factors, as previously suggested, may be cofactors in the transmethylation reaction.

(iii) The initial fall in PNMT activity in response to both dexamethasone and RU 28362 reflects pituitary suppression and lowering of adrenal medullary corticosterone levels. The return to basal levels with higher doses of dexamethasone presumably reflects its ability to mimic the high intraadrenal levels of corticosterone, an ability not shared by the selective glucocorticoid RU 28362.

(iv) Finally, in a number of ways, the effect of glucocorticoids on adrenal medullary PNMT activity in vivo is primarily indirect. In particular, the putative effect on cosubstrate availability—the predominant determinant of PNMT activity rather than enzyme level per se—appears mediated via low-affinity receptors distinct from classical GRs in the adrenal medulla. The extent to which such low-affinity receptors represent models for similar receptors in the brain, and thus the extent to which the adrenal medulla may be exploited in this regard as a window into the CNS, remains to be determined.

Reference

1.   Wong DL, Lesage A, Siddall B, et al. Glucocorticoid regulation of phenylethanolamine *N*-methyltransferase in vivo. Submitted.

Neural Actions of Steroids: When is the Genome Involved?

Bruce S. McEwen, Ph.D.

Laboratory of Neuroendocrinology, Rockefeller University, New York, New York 10021

Steroid hormones were recognized in the 1940s as having anesthetic effects. Yet in the 1960s, the discovery of intracellular DNA binding steroid receptors and the ascendency of molecular biology directed attention away from membrane actions of steroids and toward the genome. Nevertheless, when intracellular steroid receptors were discovered in brain and other tissues, electrophysiologists kept finding some quite rapid actions of steroids on neural activity. Moreover, neuroendocrine physiologists found rapid effects of steroids that appeared to be acting on the cell surface to alter release of peptide hormones and neurotransmitters. Nevertheless, various other actions of steroids required latencies of many minutes to hours, and had other characteristics of genomically mediated events.

Renewed Interest in Nongenomic Effects

Discovery of steroid receptor sites on the chloride channel of the γ-aminobutyric acid(GABA)$_A$–benzodiazepine receptor complex and the finding of progesterone effects on the mobilization of calcium ions in oocytes and spermatozoa have redirected attention toward the membrane actions of steroids. There are various examples of cell-surface actions of steroids (1), yet these actions frequently coexist with genomic effects (2). One challenge for researchers is distinguishing these effects from each other, whereas another intriguing puzzle is understanding how they interact in modulating physiological and behavioral events.

Criteria for Distinguishing Nongenomic from Genomic Effects

Distinguishing nongenomic from genomic effects of steroids involves applying a number of criteria, only a few of which are more or less foolproof. In the latter category are experiments in which a steroid is demonstrated to have an effect on a membrane or a cellular event in a preparation (e.g., a patched membrane or an isolated piece of median eminence tissue) devoid of cell nuclei. Another experimental approach for distinguishing membrane from genomic effects is attaching steroids to macromolecules to prevent them from entering the cell. Provided that steroids do not detach from the macromolecular support, the activity that steroids produce strongly implies a cell-surface site of action. Another possibility for discriminating nongenomic from genomic effects is to use time of onset of a steroid effect or to employ specific antagonists known to block intracellular receptors. Regarding time, the longer a steroid effect takes to appear and the longer it lasts when the steroid is removed, the more likely it is a genomic event. At least two possible complications can occur, however: some genomic effects can occur within minutes (e.g., inhibition of glucose transport in lymphocytes), thus one could easily miss such an effect by setting a time limit in terms of an hour or so; also, a membrane event that triggers a second messenger system may actually alter genomic activity through transacting factors phosphorylated by the second messenger system. As for specific receptor antagonists, there is every reason to believe that the binding site conformation of an intracellular receptor and of a cell-surface receptor might be similar enough to recognize the same steroid antagonists. For example, it is unclear whether receptors on the cell surface that recognize progesterone might be inhibited by RU 38486, which blocks intracellular receptors. Only when the steroid specificity is quite different (e.g., when the chloride channel of the $GABA_A$–benzodiazepine receptor binds steroids that do not bind to the intracellular progesterone receptor) can a clear distinction be made.

Estrogen and Progesterone Effects on the $GABA_A$ Receptor

The $GABA_A$ receptor exemplifies some problems encountered in distinguishing nongenomic from genomic effects. As noted, there are clear-cut membrane actions of metabolites of progesterone and deoxycorticosterone that involve a binding site on the chloride channel (1); and yet there also are in vivo actions of estradiol and progesterone on

$GABA_A$ receptor binding that are not so easy to recognize as a nongenomic or a genomic effect (3–5).

Estradiol treatment of ovariectomized female rats for 3 days causes a fall in $GABA_A$ receptor binding, which is localized to the ventromedial nuclei of the hypothalamus (VMN) and the midbrain central gray (MCG) (3,5). This treatment also causes an increase in $GABA_A$ receptor binding in the CA1 field of the hippocampus (4). Progesterone treatment in vivo, 72 hr after estrogen priming, reverses the decrease in $GABA_A$ binding in the VMN and MCG and has no effect on the increased $GABA_A$ receptor binding in the CA1 region of the hippocampus (4,5).

Are these effects nongenomic or genomic? Now, we cannot tell for sure. However, in vitro application of progesterone and 3α-hydroxy-5α-pregnan-20-one (3α-OH-DHP) to brain sections increased [^{3}H]muscimol binding more generally. This increase occurred independently of prior estrogen priming and was not restricted to specific brain regions. Moreover, whereas the in vivo effect of progesterone was seen only in females primed in vivo with estrogen, the in vitro effect was seen in both sexes (M. McCarthy, M. Schumacher, H. Coirini, A. Johnson, D.W. Pfaff, S. Schwartz-Giblin and B.S. McEwen, unpublished data). Thus, region- and sex-specific cellular events, possibly involving the genome, are likely required for the specific actions of progesterone seen in vivo, and the direct membrane effects of progesterone and progesterone metabolites are probably more transient events.

Synergistic Interactions Between Nongenomic and Genomic Effects

Another important aspect of nongenomic actions of steroids is how they interdigitate with genomic effects to regulate neural activity. We have been studying a brain system that illustrates one way in which nongenomic and genomic effects can interact (2). Oxytocin receptors are induced in the ventromedial hypothalamus of the female and the male rat by in vivo estrogen priming. During 24 to 48 hr these receptors are transported laterally into the dendrites that spread laterally from the VMN, and the oxytocin receptor field actually enlarges and spreads. The administration of progesterone induces further spread of the receptor field in the lateral direction. In contrast with the spread of receptors after estrogen priming, which takes many hours, the progesterone effect is rapid, occurring within 1 hr. Moreover, the action of progesterone can take place in vitro in frozen and thawed sections prepared for autoradiography (2). This effect is produced by 100 nM progesterone but not by estradiol, choles-

Progesterone (P)

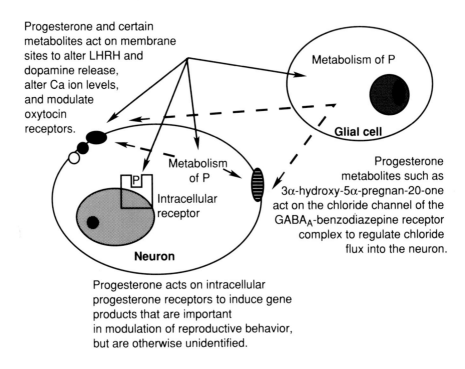

Progesterone and certain metabolites act on membrane sites to alter LHRH and dopamine release, alter Ca ion levels, and modulate oxytocin receptors.

Metabolism of P

Glial cell

Metabolism of P

Intracellular receptor

Neuron

Progesterone metabolites such as 3α-hydroxy-5α-pregnan-20-one act on the chloride channel of the GABA$_A$-benzodiazepine receptor complex to regulate chloride flux into the neuron.

Progesterone acts on intracellular progesterone receptors to induce gene products that are important in modulation of reproductive behavior, but are otherwise unidentified.

| Seconds | Minutes | Hours | Days | Years |

Nongenomic   Genomic

Figure 1. Schematic summary of the known and postulated nongenomic mechanisms of action of progesterone and its metabolites in neural tissue, as well as the genomic actions of progesterone via intracellular receptors. Steroids such as progesterone have effects via both genomic and nongenomic routes. The nongenomic effects may involve the parent steroid or one of the metabolites generated locally in the brain or arriving at the brain via the circulation. Note the time line, which indicates that genomic effects have longer onset delays and last longer, whereas nongenomic effects are much more rapid in onset and offset when the steroid is removed. However, latencies and durations on the order of minutes may be more difficult to sort out. LHRH, luteinizing hormone–releasing hormone. (Reprinted with permission from ref. 1.)

terol or 3α-OH-DHP, which indicates that the effect involves a steroid-specific action that differs from the activation of the chloride channel on the GABA$_A$ receptor.

The nature of the membrane receptor mediating this effect is unknown, as is the mechanism for the rapid spread of the oxytocin receptor field. One possibility is that this effect represents a rapid activation of a transport mechanism, but this is less likely because the in vitro effect occurs in previously frozen brain sections. Another possibility is that the apparent spread of oxytocin receptors is actually the conversion of low-affinity or even cryptic receptors to high-affinity ones that bind the labeled oxytocin antagonist. In either case, the effect is important because only after progesterone treatment of estrogen-primed female rats can oxytocin activate female sexual behavior (2). Curiously, male rats do not show female sexual behavior after estrogen plus progesterone priming; although they show estrogen induction of oxytocin receptors in the VMN, there is no effect of progesterone to increase the oxytocin receptor field (H. Coirini, M. Schumacher and B.S. McEwen, unpublished data).

Figure 1 summarizes some of the actions of the versatile steroid hormone, progesterone, via genomic and cell-surface actions, and notes the criterion of time course for distinguishing rapid membrane effects from delayed and prolonged nongenomic effects.

References

1. McEwen BS. Non-genomic and genomic effects of steroids on neural activity. *Trends Pharmacol Sci* 1991;12:141–147.
2. Schumacher M, Coirini H, Pfaff DW, et al. Behavioral effects of progesterone associated with rapid modulation of oxytocin receptors. *Science* 1990;250:691–694.
3. O'Connor L, Nock B, McEwen BS. Regional specificity of gamma-aminobutyric acid receptor regulation by estradiol. *Neuroendocrinology* 1988;47:473–481.
4. Schumacher M, Coirini H, McEwen BS. Regulation of high-affinity GABA$_A$ receptors in the dorsal hippocampus by estradiol and progesterone. *Brain Res* 1989;487:178–183.
5. Schumacher M, Coirini H, McEwen BS. Regulation of high-affinity GABA$_A$ receptors in specific brain regions by ovarian hormones. *Neuroendocrinology* 1989;50:315–320.

II

Steroid Regulation and Brain Function

Negative Feedback of Glucocorticoids on the Brain and Pituitary: Role of Feedback and its Interactions with Circadian and Stress Signals

Mary F. Dallman, Ph.D., and Susan F. Akana, Ph.D.

Department of Physiology, University of California,
San Francisco, California 94143

Three major factors interact to determine the secretory rate of the hypothalamic corticotropin-releasing factors (CRFs) CRF_{41} and arginine vasopressin (AVP): a circadian rhythm in basal activity, stimulus(stress)-induced responses, and corticosteroid negative feedback inhibition. Each factor influences the level of hypothalamic activity caused by the other two. CRFs in turn determine adrenocorticotropic hormone (ACTH) and corticosteroid secretion in the adrenocortical system (ACS).

Basal activity in the rat ACS peaks at the time of "lights out," when daily activity begins in this nocturnal animal. Peak activity is driven by the suprachiasmatic nuclei. Lesions of these nuclei (1), as well as lesions of the CRF/AVP neurons in the paraventricular nuclei (PVN) result in constant low ACTH and corticosterone (B) levels. In contrast, values of ACTH and B at the trough of the rhythm, at "lights on," are essentially zero, and appear to result from the lack of hypothalamic input to the pituitary ACTH-secreting cells (2). Because responsiveness of ACTH secretion to CRFs is the same during the trough and peak of the rhythm (3), diurnal changes in the magnitude of ACTH secretion are mediated in the CNS, not at the pituitary.

Stimulus(stress)-induced ACTH secretion can occur at any time of day. However, the magnitude of ACTH secretion elicited by stress depends on stimulus intensity and on the time in the circadian cycle at which it is applied. ACTH responses to stress are greatest at the trough of the cycle and least at the peak of the cycle; this change in magnitude of the response is not mediated by B levels, because the change occurs in both intact and bilaterally adrenalectomized (ADX) rats (4). Furthermore, stress facilitates responsiveness of the ACS to subsequent stress (5).

The effect of glucocorticoid feedback on ACS function can readily be observed after ADX, which removes the steroid signal. ADX results in immediate hypersecretion of ACTH and rapid increases in CRF and AVP mRNA and peptide synthesis in parvocellular neurons of the PVN. Increased CRF secretion stimulates corticotroph proliferation, proopiomelanocortin mRNA synthesis and ACTH secretion from the pituitary. Within 5 days, ACTH is elevated tenfold at all times of day but maintains the usual circadian rhythm (4). Replacement of ADX rats with B maintains CRFs and ACTH in the normal range (2).

Provision of constant plasma B levels in ADX rats revealed a *diurnal rhythm in sensitivity* of ACTH to B, with greatest feedback sensitivity during the trough and least during the peak (3). The effect of B on trough ACTH is mediated in the CNS, not the pituitary (6), probably by association of the steroid with type I, high-affinity mineralocorticoid receptors (MRs). In contrast, at the peak, the feedback effect is probably mediated by B acting through both MR and type II, lower-affinity glucocorticoid receptors (GRs) (7). This scenario has experimental support and accounts for the decreased sensitivity of ACTH to inhibition by B that occurs between trough and peak times of day.

The ACS of the *intact rat* is highly sensitive to small increases above normal in B. In intact rats, implantation of B pellets that raise trough B by 2 or 5 µg/dl for 5 days results in decrements in peak B of 4 or 10 µg/dl, so that the mean daily B concentration is held constant between 5 and 6 µg/dl (8). A constant (as opposed to phasic) mean B signal of 5 µg/dl, however, blocks diurnal rhythms in ACTH and B, inhibits ACTH responses to stress and decreases thymus weight, clear signs of glucocorticoid excess.

In direct contrast to chronic B treatment, *chronic stress* appears to facilitate activity in central neural components of the ACS, thus balancing the elevated feedback signal provided by stress-induced B secretion (5). A decrease in thymus weight, of similar magnitude to that seen after chronic B, occurs 5 days after giving streptozotocin and causing the chronic stress of diabetes in rats. However, with stress, the chronically elevated B does *not* inhibit either diurnal rhythms in B or the magnitude of the stress response; the ACTH response to stress is actually enhanced compared with control rats. Because pituitary and adrenal responses to CRFs and ACTH are normal, the facilitatory effect of stress on ACS function must be in the CNS.

We tested directly for a facilitatory effect of stress on subsequent ACS function using cyanoketone (CK), a drug that partly inhibits the activity of a steroid-synthesizing enzyme, EC 1.1.1.51. Treatment with CK for several days results in rats that are unable to secrete B acutely in response to stress, although they retain normal diurnal rhythms in B (9). To determine whether prior stress facilitates subsequent ACS responses, we exposed CK-treated rats and their vehicle-treated controls to stress and measured the effects on subsequent ACS function. Some groups of rats were restrained during the "lights-on" period and sampled at the time of the peak ("lights off") for "basal" and stress (30-min restraint) ACTH and B levels. Other groups of rats were stressed during the "lights-off" period and sampled under "basal" and stress conditions at the trough of the rhythm ("lights on").

These experiments revealed clear evidence that *prior stress facilitates* the central control of ACTH secretion. However, the effect of facilitation on ACTH secretion depended on the time of day at which it was examined. Peak "basal" ACTH levels were significantly elevated in CK-treated rats stressed during the "lights-on" period; however, there was no additional stress-induced facilitation of the ACTH response to restraint stress at this time of day. In contrast, trough "basal" ACTH levels were essentially normal in CK-treated rats stressed during the night; however, there was marked facilitation of the ACTH response to stress in such rats at this time of day. Vehicle-treated rats responded similarly to restraint whether or not they had been exposed to prior stress.

These results provide direct evidence that when rats are stressed, there is facilitation of the subsequent drive to ACTH, which is usually balanced by the inhibitory signal provided by corticosterone. The expression of stress-induced facilitation on ACTH is determined by the diurnal rhythm in ACS activity. Consequently, the facilitatory effect must be in the CNS and is probably at a site proximal to the final CRF output pathway.

What is the role of glucocorticoid negative feedback on the brain in ACS function? The ACS acts on peripheral targets through glucocorticoids. Every mammalian cell type contains GRs, and glucocorticoids exert myriad effects on tissues throughout the body by acting in a *dose-dependent fashion* through the combination of a steroid with its receptor. For a normal, basal level of cellular function, the daily occupation of GR must be held within a narrow range; too little or too much results in pathological changes. Under conditions of stress, more glucocorticoids are required, for instance, for adequate gluconeogenesis and substrate mobilization to meet increased demand, or to modulate stress responses that occur in other systems (hormonal or immune; 10). Glucocorticoid feedback on the CNS allows controlled changes in circulating corticosteroid levels within ranges appropriate for varied demands.

Glucocorticoid *feedback functions at all times* of day, under both basal and stress conditions. The complete absence of B (ADX) stimulates remarkable increases in CRF synthesis and secretion. However, our studies with intact rats given small amounts of extra B suggest that even when mean daily levels of B are normal, a constant B signal is detrimental to the animal, causing thymic atrophy and a number of other changes from normal. We suspect that this occurs because the diurnal trough in B has been elevated to the point at which GRs are *continually* occupied at a low level, in contrast to normal; normally, during 25% to 30% of the day there is essentially *no occupancy* of GRs (11). This situation is achieved by the inhibitory effect of B acting through occupancy of MRs. Normally, approximately 70% occupancy of GRs occurs during the peak of the rhythm (11). This finding appears to satisfy the glucocorticoid requirements of the peripheral tissues and also maintains peak ACTH values at normal levels. Glucocorticoid feedback shapes the circadian input from the suprachiasmatic nuclei through occupancy of MRs and GRs, thus maintaining normal ACTH (and B).

Stress, which increases glucocorticoid secretion, also facilitates subsequent activity in the ACS. However, glucocorticoids secreted at the time of stress balance the facilitation, leaving the ACS continually responsive, but not overresponsive to subsequent stimulation. This inhibitory action of glucocorticoids protects against markedly overshooting appropriate levels of GR occupancy in target tissues. Most of the physiological feedback actions of B are exerted on brain components of the ACS. However, with prolonged elevations in B produced by intense, chronic stress, feedback at the corticotroph may occur. The pituitary is less sensitive to feedback than the brain (6) and probably provides an emergency brake on the ACS when brain mechanisms are overwhelmed by stress.

References

1. Cascio CS, Shinsako J, Dallman MF. The suprachiasmatic nuclei stimulate evening ACTH secretion in the rat. *Brain Res* 1987;423:173–179.

2. Dallman MF, Akana SF, Levin N, et al. Corticosterone replacement in adrenalectomized rats: insights into the regulation of ACTH secretion. In: Rose FC, ed. *The control of the hypothalamo-pituitary-adrenocortical axis.* Madison, CT: International Universities Press, 1989;95–116.

3. Akana SF, Cascio CS, Du J-Z, et al. Reset of feedback in the adrenocortical system: an apparent shift in sensitivity of adrenocorticotropin to inhibition by corticosterone between morning and evening. *Endocrinology* 1986;119:2325–2332.

4. Bradbury MJ, Cascio CS, Scribner KA, et al. Stress-induced adrenocorticotropin secretion: diurnal responses and decreases during stress in the evening are not dependent on corticosterone. *Endocrinology* 1991;128:680–688.

5. Scribner KA, Walker C-D, Cascio CS, et al. Chronic streptozotocin diabetes in rats facilitates the acute stress response without altering pituitary or adrenal responsiveness to secretagogues. *Endocrinology* 1991;129:99–108.

6. Levin N, Shinsako J, Dallman MF. Corticosterone acts on the brain to inhibit adrenalectomy-induced ACTH secretion. *Endocrinology* 1988;122:694–704.

7. Dallman MF, Levin N, Cascio CS, et al. Pharmacological evidence that the inhibition of diurnal adrenocorticotropin secretion by corticosteroids is mediated via type I corticosterone-preferring receptors. *Endocrinology* 1989;124:2844–2850.

8. Akana SF, Bradbury MJ, Cascio CS, et al. Low levels of exogenous corticosterone (B) impair regulation of ACTH and B in intact rats. *Endocrinology* 1991;128A:41.

9. Akana SF, Dallman MF. Stress facilitates subsequent activity in the adrenocortical system. *Soc Neurosci Abstr* 1990;16:698.

10. Munck A, Guyre PM, Holbrook NJ. Physiological function of glucocorticoids in stress and their relation to pharmacological actions. *Endocr Rev* 1984;5:25–48.

11. Reul JHMH, de Kloet ER. Two receptor systems for corticosterone in rat brain: microdistribution and differential occupation. *Endocrinology* 1985;117:2505–2511.

Interplay Between Glucocorticoid Receptors and Neuronal Pathways in Controlling Circadian and Stress Response Patterns

H. Akil, Ph.D., S. Kwak, Ph.D., I. Morano, Ph.D., J. Herman, Ph.D.,
L. Taylor, Ph.D., and S. Watson, M.D., Ph.D.

Mental Health Research Institute, University of Michigan,
Ann Arbor, Michigan 48109

The responsiveness of the hypothalamic-pituitary-adrenal axis (HPA) must be tightly controlled to produce rapid activation of synthesis and release of adrenal glucocorticoids, as well as rapid termination of this response. This situation is achieved via a number of neuronal brain circuits as well as genomic and nongenomic actions of the glucocorticoids themselves, which control the level of activity of the axis. In addition, stress responses are elaborated against a circadian rhythm of basal glucocorticoid secretion. This rhythm is coupled to activity rather than to light, and peaks at the onset of awakening (i.e., in the early morning in humans and the early evening in nocturnal animals). Little is known about the central brain mechanisms that orchestrate this rhythm. Even less is known about the relationship between the mechanisms that control the HPA circadian rhythm and those that control stress responsiveness (activation and termination).

This chapter briefly describes the brain elements that control stress responses and provides an overview of the neuronal circuits that may play a role in controlling basal tone as well as stress responses. The overview is followed by a description of the changes in corticotropin-releasing hormone (CRH) gene expression across the circadian rhythm, and the role of glucocorticoids in shaping this pattern of responses.

I. *The brain elements* critical to the control of stress activation include the neurons of the paraventricular nucleus of the hypothalamus (PVN), which express two critical peptides—CRH [the major adrenocortico-tropin hormone (ACTH) secretagogue] and vasopressin (AVP), which amplifies the effects of CRH. In addition, two corticosteroid receptors, the glucocorticoid receptor (GR) and the mineralocorticoid receptor (MR) are critical in mediating negative steroid feedback on the axis. In situ hybridization studies (1) demonstrate that GRs and MRs are expressed throughout the brain, with certain areas such as the hippocampus particularly rich in receptor mRNAs. The in situ findings are generally consonant with receptor autoradiography studies demonstrating high levels of GR and MR binding in these regions.

GRs and MRs are cytosolic proteins complexed with the heat-shock proteins (such as HSP-90). On binding steroid ligands, GRs become transformed and translocate to the nucleus to produce various genomic effects. The interaction with the HSP-90 complex is critical for the proper functioning of these receptors. In collaboration with William Pratt, we have begun to define the specific site of GR/HSP-90 interaction, and have located this interface to a particular carboxy terminal sequence of the steroid binding domain of GRs (2).

II. *The neuronal circuits* that coordinate the interplay between these elements are under investigation in our laboratories (3). We have focused on the circuits that may mediate steroid feedback inhibition, which arise in the hippocampus, and somehow modulate the CRH neurons in the PVN. Lesion studies coupled with quantitative in situ hybridization of PVN CRH suggest that the hippocampus may exert a negative inhibitory effect on CRH. Hippocampectomy leads to an increase in CRH and AVP mRNA in the PVN, an increase in ACTH release into the general circulation, and an elevation in plasma corticosterone. This pattern is highly unusual. Typically, an increase in plasma corticosteroids leads to a *decrease* in CRH mRNA. The hippocampectomized animal appeared to *lack negative steroid feedback,* displaying an elevated HPA tone, without consequent inhibition of the releasing factors. These findings, along with previous findings from the work of a number of groups of investigators suggest that the hippocampus plays a critical role in negative feedback. In addition, these results suggest that a pathway connects the hippocampus to the PVN. More discrete lesion studies have eliminated certain potential connections and have pointed to the following pathway: a projection from the hippocampus via the lateral fornix would end in the bed nucleus of the stria terminalis (BNST), where it would synapse onto a second neuron arising in the BNST and projecting to the PVN. This potential pathway currently is being confirmed by using anterograde and retrograde tracing methods.

An interesting observation that arose from the hippocampectomy studies was that the effect of the lesion on CRH mRNA was not equal at different times of the day. Whereas the phenomena described in the text above (such as an increase in CRH mRNA postlesion) were seen in the morning, the effects were clearly blunted in the evening. Thus, the hippocampus appeared to exhibit an inhibitory effect on *basal CRH expression,* and this effect was *differential across the circadian rhythm.* Could the hippocampus play a role in shaping the circadian rhythm of the HPA axis by affecting the level of CRH mRNA? This question was difficult to address because little was known about the pattern of CRH mRNA in the PVN in relation to the known daily rhythm of glucocorticoids. We therefore undertook a series of studies to investigate this issue.

III. *Circadian rhythm:* It is well established that in rats, glucocorticoid levels in plasma peak in the evening at about "lights off." ACTH, the pituitary hormone that controls glucocorticoid synthesis and release, also exhibits a circadian rhythm, albeit less clear-cut than the steroid rhythm. In our studies, we found ACTH to peak slightly before the corticosterone high point. However, proopiomelanocortin mRNA levels in the pituitary do not appear to change, and the peptide content of the gland does not appear to exhibit any oscillations. Thus, pituitary changes in ACTH plasma levels presumably reflect the altered drive levels exerted by the hypothalamic secretagogues—particularly CRH and AVP.

Could CRH mRNA change rapidly enough to exhibit meaningful oscillations over the course of the day? Preliminary studies showed that this message was capable of rapid perturbations, presumably because of the small size of the pool. We therefore undertook a series of studies to examine CRH mRNA levels across the rhythm and to investigate the possible role of corticosteroid feedback in shaping the CRH daily pattern (4).

Our studies demonstrated that indeed, CRH mRNA levels exhibited substantial oscillations across the daily cycle. The pattern was reliable, appearing consistently across 3 separate replications. This rhythm, however, was more complex than the sinusoidal rhythm seen for the plasma hormones. Rather, this rhythm rose steadily throughout the morning hours, reaching a peak before "lights off." Then, as the glucocorticoid levels reached their own peak, CRH mRNA levels in the PVN dropped sharply, then rebounded within 2 to 3 hr and underwent another "resetting" with the change in lighting in the morning. Could the steep rise in glucocorticoids at "lights off" be responsible for the coincidental drop in CRH mRNA? In other words, could steroids, via negative feedback, shape the pattern of their own secretion?

To address this issue, we adrenalectomized rats and compared their CRH mRNA to sham-operated animals. Based on past studies, we anticipated that CRH mRNA levels would be elevated. But would the *pattern* be altered?

Adrenalectomy did not prevent the sharp drop in CRH mRNA seen at the onset of dark, suggesting that this decrease was caused by neuronal events that inhibit transcription of that gene, rather than by short or intermediate glucocorticoid feedback effects on that transcription. A change in the CRH mRNA pattern, however, was seen in the morning: instead of the gradual rise over several hours seen in the sham animals, the CRH mRNA levels in adrenalectomized rats increased sharply. This finding suggests that glucocorticoids indeed are important in patterning the daily gradual rise in CRH message that takes place in the morning (i.e., during the rat's rest period). We then asked, Is the *pattern of corticosteroids* important in controlling the pattern of CRH mRNA during the daylight hours? To address this question, we adrenalectomized rats and treated them with steroid pellets, which yielded a steady level of corticosterone across the day (a procedure adopted from F. Dalman and coworkers). Of particular interest was a group of rats that received a steady dose of steroids equal to the *normal mean daily level* in a control animal. Thus, these animals were exposed to the same overall level of hormone but lacked a circadian rhythm. Interestingly, *their CRH mRNA appeared normal.* This series of circadian studies led to the following conclusions:

a) CRH mRNA levels exhibit a distinctive circadian rhythm. In most cases, rises in CRH mRNA *anticipate* the increased CRH secretion which drives the pituitary and adrenal components.

b) The pattern of this rhythm appears controlled primarily by *neuronal* rather than glucocorticoid influences.

c) Glucocorticoids control the overall level of CRH expression. They also control the *rate of rise* of CRH mRNA in the daytime hours.

d) However, the *oscillation* of glucocorticoids *is not critical* to this process. Rather, a minimal level of steroids is both necessary and sufficient to impose its influence on the CRH tone.

In sum, it is clear that the brain "reads" levels of stress steroids and uses this information to set the overall basal tone of the HPA axis. Although direct genomic mechanisms via glucocorticoid receptors can explain the overall effects of stress steroids on CRH mRNA, these mechanisms do not explain how the presence of steroids in the morning specifically modulates the CRH rhythm. We tentatively propose *a role of the hippocampus* in the neuronal patterning of the basal circadian rhythm of CRH. This hypothesis, which certainly requires direct testing, is based on our findings (reported in the text above) of the differential effects of hippocampectomy across the day; on the high expression within the hippocampus of the MR receptor, which is exquisitely sensitive to low levels of corticosteroids (found in the morning); as well as on a number of convergent lines of evidence not reported here (including some formulations of E.R. de Kloet and co-workers). The hippocampus thus may serve as an integrator between the molecular elements responsible for activation or inhibition of the stress axis (CRH and corticosteroid receptors, respectively). The hippocampus also may coordinate the function of these elements within a neuronal context that defines a circadian pattern of activity. This proposed role *in controlling basal tone and rhythmicity* must be distinguished from the function, suggested by other investigators (such as B.S. McEwen, R. Sapolsky and their colleagues), of the hippocampus as a key factor in the termination of stress.

Thus, to bring about tight control of the production of its highly potent final products, adrenal glucocorticoids, the stress axis uses the subtle and complex interplay between neuronal circuitry and hormonal mechanisms. Such an interplay is evident both in terms of a basal tone that oscillates along with the rest-activity cycle, and the activated state in response to numerous stressors. Much work remains in order to understand the coordination of these events.

References

1. Herman JP, Patel PD, Akil H, et al. Localization and regulation of glucocorticoid and mineralocorticoid receptor mRNAs in the hippocampal formation of the rat. *Mol Endocrinol* 1989;3:1886–1894.
2. Dalman FC, Scherrer L, Taylor L, et al. Localization of the HSP90 binding site within the hormone binding domain of the glucocorticoid receptor by peptide competition. *J Biol Chem* 1991;266:3482–3490.
3. Herman JP, Schafer MK-H, Young EA, et al. Evidence for hippocampal regulation of neuroendocrine neurons of the hypothalamo-pituitary-adrenocortical axis. *J Neurosci* 1989;9:3072–3082.
4. Kwak SP, Young EA, Morano I, et al. Diurnal corticotropin-releasing hormone mRNA variation in the hypothalamus exhibits a rhythm distinct from that of plasma corticosterone. *Neuroendocrinology* 1991;(in press).

Cell Specificity in the Control of Proopiomelanocortin Gene Expression

Jacques Drouin, D.Sc., Mona Nemer, Ph.D., Yu Lin Sun, Ph.D., and Marc Therrien

Laboratory of Molecular Genetics, Clinical Research Institute of Montréal, Montréal (Québec), Canada H2W 1R7

Pituitary proopiomelanocortin (POMC) and, in particular, one of its processing products, adrenocorticotropic hormone (ACTH), play a major role in the control of steroid biosynthesis by the adrenal glands. To ensure tight control of their levels, the biosynthesis of POMC and the secretion of POMC-derived products are regulated by many factors and hormones (for review see ref. 1). In particular, adrenal glucocorticoids exert a negative feedback on both of these processes in anterior pituitary POMC–expressing corticotroph cells. However, glucocorticoids do not usually have any effect on POMC expression in the other pituitary cells that express this gene, namely the α-melanocyte-stimulating hormone–producing melanotroph cells. We investigated the molecular basis for this specificity in glucocorticoid feedback as well as for the specific expression of the POMC gene in pituitary corticotroph and melanotroph cells.

Multiple Factors Control Cell-Specific Expression of the POMC Gene

The rat POMC (rPOMC) gene encodes the precursor of ACTH, β-endorphin and the melanotropins, and is the first hormone gene activated during fetal pituitary development (1). POMC expression is restricted to corticotroph and melanotroph cells of the pituitary gland. The POMC gene also is expressed at low levels in some nonpituitary tissues. The hypothalamus is the only extrapituitary tissue in which the pattern of POMC gene transcription appears similar to that in the

37

pituitary gland. Other POMC-expressing tissues—including the testis, ovary, placenta, and some lymphoid cells—mostly contain a smaller form of POMC mRNA that does not encode for the complete POMC precursor (1,2). Thus, the activity of the pituitary POMC gene promoter appears restricted to that tissue and to a small population of hypothalamic neurons. We have taken advantage of the AtT-20 cell line (corticotroph tumor cell line) to study in detail the molecular basis for cell-specific regulation of the POMC promoter. This cell line originates from a pituitary tumor that expressed POMC; its pattern of POMC processing and regulation is similar to that of anterior pituitary corticotroph cells. Thus, analysis of the POMC promoter in this cell line should provide a model for the identification of factors involved in cell-specific POMC expression and in early stages of pituitary development.

Previously, in our laboratory using transfection (3) and transgenic mice (4) experiments, we showed that no more than 543 bp of the 5'-flanking gene sequence are required for cell-specific expression of the rPOMC gene. Using DNAase I footprinting, gel retardation and replacement mutagenesis, we showed that the activity of the rPOMC promoter results from the synergistic interactions of at least 10 different regulatory elements, which are recognized by at least 10 different nuclear proteins (5). Some of these nuclear proteins are related to AP-1, COUP and Sp1 transcription factors, whereas others require further characterization. This complex promoter organization is in contrast with promoters of other pituitary-specific genes such as those encoding growth hormone and prolactin. One of the POMC regulatory elements confers corticotroph-specific activity in transfection experiments. This element is recognized in vitro by at least three classes of nuclear proteins present in AtT-20 cells. None of these proteins is related to Pit-1/GHF-1, which is responsible for cell-specific expression of the growth hormone and prolactin genes. Point mutation analysis of this element indicates that only one class of nuclear proteins is responsible for activity. Furthermore, these proteins do not appear to be present in other cell extracts. The properties of these cell-specific nuclear proteins are currently under investigation by molecular cloning to determine their role in POMC transcription and in pituitary development.

Glucocorticoid Repression of POMC Gene Transcription

Glucocorticoids, synthesized in response to POMC-derived ACTH, exert a specific negative feedback on ACTH secretion and POMC transcription in the anterior pituitary (1). We previously identified in the proximal POMC promoter an in vitro binding site for the glucocorticoid receptor (GR), and provided evidence that this receptor binding site might be involved in glucocorticoid repression of POMC (6). This GR binding site is somewhat similar in DNA sequence to the well-characterized glucocorticoid response element (GRE). GREs behave like hormone-dependent regulatory elements of transcription, and their properties have been well characterized (7).

The POMC negative GRE (nGRE) sequence contains important differences compared with conserved GRE sequences. Because the same transcription factor, GR, appears to mediate repression of POMC and stimulation of transcription of GRE-containing genes, we tested whether differences in the nGRE sequence compared with GRE are in part responsible for differences in the transcriptional properties of nGRE and GRE. When the POMC nGRE sequence was mutated to a consensus GRE by site-directed mutagenesis, the mutated POMC promoter was converted from glucocorticoid repressed to glucocorticoid inducible. Thus, the specific DNA sequence of the binding site is crucial for its positive or negative hormone response.

In view of this profound difference, we tested whether GR interacts differently with nGRE and with consensus GRE. Using purified rat liver GR in a gel retardation assay, we characterized a novel GR:DNA interaction with the POMC binding site. Whereas typical GREs bind GR dimers (7), the POMC binding site appeared to bind three GR subunits that interact with both sides of the DNA helix. Formation of these novel complexes appeared to correlate with glucocorticoid repression of POMC, because mutants that do not form these complexes are not glucocorticoid repressed. Thus, the novel GR:nGRE complex appears to be involved in glucocorticoid repression of POMC. However, our analyses indicated that a classical factor displacement model or a dominant repressor model do not appear to be involved in hormone-dependent repression. The interaction between GRs bound to the nGRE and other factors/elements in the POMC promoter is under investigation in order to define the molecular basis for glucocorticoid repression.

References

1.   Drouin J, Sun YL, Nemer M. Regulatory elements of the pro-opiomelanocortin gene: pituitary specificity and glucocorticoid repression. *Trends Endocrinol Metab* 1990;1:219–225.

2. Jeannotte L, Burbach JPH, Drouin J. Unusual pro-opiomelanocortin ribonucleic acids in extrapituitary tissues: intronless transcripts in testes and long Poly(A) tails in hypothalamus. *Mol Endocrinol* 1987;1:749–757.

3. Jeannotte L, Trifiro MA, Plante RK, et al. Tissue-specific activity of the pro-opiomelanocortin gene promoter. *Mol Cell Biol* 1987;7:4058–4064.

4. Tremblay Y, Tretjakoff I, Peterson A, et al. Pituitary-specific expression and glucocorticoid regulation of a pro-opiomelanocortin (POMC) fusion gene in transgenic mice. *Proc Natl Acad Sci USA* 1988;85:8890–8894.

5. Therrien M, Drouin J. Pituitary pro-opiomelanocortin gene expression requires synergistic interactions of several regulatory elements. *Mol Cell Biol* 1991;11:1545–1583.

6. Drouin J, Trifiro MA, Plante RK, et al. Glucocorticoid receptor binding to a specific DNA sequence is required for hormone-dependent inhibition of pro-opiomelanocortin gene transcription. *Mol Cell Biol* 1989;9:5305–5314.

7. Beato M. Gene regulation by steroid hormones. *Cell* 1989;56:335–344.

Steroid Regulation of Nerve Growth Factor Biosynthesis in the CNS

*I. Mocchetti, Ph.D., F.-Y. Sun, Ph.D., M. Fabrazzo, M.D., Ph.D., and E. Costa, M.D.

*Department of Anatomy and Cell Biology, Fidia-Georgetown Institute for the Neurosciences, Georgetown University School of Medicine, Washington, DC 20007

Adrenal steroids have been shown to be involved in neuroendocrine regulation of the hypothalamic-pituitary-adrenocortical axis (HPA) in response to stress, and in mechanisms of learning and memory (1). A great deal of research effort in the last few years has focused on the possibility that steroids also might be important regulators of brain function and trophic processes (1) operative in neuronal plasticity. Recently, we and other investigators have shown that adrenal steroids, released during stress, increase the content of nerve growth factor (NGF) mRNA and NGF in selected brain structures (2,3). Because NGF, along with other neuronal growth factors, is assumed to participate in neuronal trophism and regeneration, we investigated whether steroids modulate synaptic plasticity by increasing the production of NGF. NGF is synthesized, stored and released from CNS storage sites. Therefore, by learning whether and how these processes can be enhanced pharmacologically, we can develop appropriate drugs and establish the basis for a therapy directed toward improving the efficiency of neuronal plasticity in the repair of pathological and traumatic insults that hinder CNS function.

Because in adrenalectomized rats hippocampal NGF immunoreactivity is reduced, it was inferred that adrenal steroids might regulate the production of NGF in specific brain structures (2). We investigated whether dexamethasone and reserpine, two pharmacological agents that enhance blood steroid levels, increase NGF gene expression in the young adult rat CNS. Dexamethasone is a synthetic glucocorticoid that can be administered to mimic the level of plasma adrenocortical steroids occurring during stress (4). Reserpine has been demonstrated to activate the HPA (5,6) and to increase blood corticosterone content for about 15 hr (3). Both dexamethasone [0.5 mg/kg, subcutaneously (s.c.)] and reserpine administration (2 mg/kg, s.c.) elicited a two- to threefold increase in the amount of cortical NGF mRNA (Table 1). The NGF mRNA increase induced by dexamethasone or reserpine appears exclusively localized to the cerebral cortex because the NGF mRNA content of the other brain structures tested failed to change (3).

To clarify the mechanism of reserpine effect on NGF biosynthesis, we tested whether this alkaloid could increase cortical NGF mRNA content in adrenalectomized rats. Indeed, in such rats reserpine failed to increase cortical NGF mRNA (Table 1) as well as plasma corticosterone levels (3). Hence, this lack of effect of reserpine suggests that HPA activation might be a plausible explanation for the drug action on cortical NGF mRNA expression. The time course profile of the reserpine-induced changes of cortical NGF mRNA content showed that the increase is maximal (three- to fourfold) 9 hr after the administration, whereas dexamethasone

Table 1. Stimuli regulating NGF mRNA content in the rat brain

Stimulus	Brain area	NGF mRNA (percent of control)
Dexamethasone	Cerebral cortex	250* ± 22
Reserpine	Cerebral cortex	320* ± 20
Bicuculline	Hippocampus	270* ± 8
Reserpine/ADX	Cerebral cortex	90 ± 10
Bicuculline/ADX	Hippocampus	115 ± 28

Male Sprague-Dawley rats were injected with dexamethasone (0.5 mg/kg, s.c.) and sacrificed 3 hr later. Sham or 7-day-adrenalectomized (ADX) Sprague-Dawley rats were treated with reserpine (2 mg/kg, s.c.) or bicuculline (0.4 mg/kg, intravenously) and sacrificed 9 or 3 hr later, respectively. NGF mRNA was determined by Northern blot analysis as previously described (3,16). The relative amount of NGF mRNA detected in the blots was estimated in arbitrary units (16), which are defined by the ratio of the peak densitometric area of NGF mRNA and cyclophilin mRNA (7) hybridization bands. Data expressed as percentage of control values and are means ± SEM of 3 independent determinations (n = 3 for each group). *$p < 0.01$ vs. control (ANOVA and Dunnett's test).

elicited the maximum increase 3 hr after the injection (3). This increase was not due to a nonspecific change in the total mRNA synthesis, because the NGF mRNA content failed to change in other brain areas, and the cortical content of the mRNA encoding for the stable structural protein cyclophilin (7) was unchanged by the drug treatment.

Cortical NGF protein accumulates with a similar time course. Whereas dexamethasone treatment elicited a significant increase in NGF protein 6 and 9 hr after the injection, reserpine effect was observed 12, 18 and 24 hr after drug administration, and returned to the control level within 36 hr (3). The latency time for the NGF mRNA and protein response to dexamethasone is faster compared with that elicited by reserpine. This finding might reflect a direct brain action of dexamethasone that contrasts the indirect action of reserpine, which operates via a cascade of events including the release of endogenous glucocorticoids from the adrenal gland. Therefore, it is not surprising that the increase of NGF mRNA occurs as early as 1 hr after the injection of dexamethasone, and that the levels of NGF mRNA return to basal values at 9 hr (3). This time course contrasts the duration of the reserpine effect, which is about 15 hr. At 24 hr, NGF mRNA content as well as plasma corticosterone content return to basal levels (3).

The difference in the latency time for the steroid-induced increase of NGF mRNA and protein reflects the time delay required for mRNA processing, translation and posttranslational modification. The NGF protein increase follows that of NGF mRNA. Other possibilities may exist as well. For instance, glucocorticoids might affect the half-life of the newly synthesized NGF protein, which could be prolonged by an action of the steroids on the stability of the NGF protein. Thus, steroids could inhibit either the enzymatic degradation of NGF or the binding and retrograde transport of the NGF receptor complex. Because in our experimental model, the increase in NGF protein always followed the increase in NGF mRNA (3), it appears that the activation of NGF gene expression might be the mechanism whereby steroids increase cortical NGF protein content.

The increased availability of NGF might provide protection against steroid-induced neurotoxicity (8) or maintain neuronal viability. During limbic seizure, NGF expression has been described to be enhanced in specific brain areas (9). These data suggest that NGF gene expression is activated via stimulation of specific neuronal circuitry. However, during epileptiform activity, there is a concomitant increase of adrenal corticosteroid levels. Therefore, the seizure-mediated increase in NGF expression also could be due to the increased plasma corticosteroids. We tested this hypothesis by injecting the GABAergic receptor antagonist bicuculline at the dose known to elicit seizure activity [0.4 mg/kg, intraperitoneally (i.p.)]. One hour after the injection, NGF mRNA content was increased in the hippocampus (Table 1). Moreover, this increase was abolished in adrenalectomized rats (Table 1) although bicuculline could still elicit seizure activity. These preliminary findings suggest that adrenal steroids might be the common mechanism whereby NGF expression is induced in the CNS by drugs that elicit a stressful situation.

Type I steroid receptors for mineralocorticoids as well as type II receptors for glucocorticoids are expressed in the brain (10). Therefore, these steroids can induce the expression of the NGF gene, as well as that of other genes in different brain structures. We have found, however, that NGF expression is enhanced only in the cerebral cortex after dexamethasone treatment, and only in the hippocampus after bicuculline injection. These data suggest that NGF expression in different brain areas might be modulated either by transsynaptic mechanisms activated by specific steroid receptor occupancy or by a direct stimulation of specific steroid receptors located in selective neuronal populations. Type I receptors appear to be abundant in the hippocampus and low in the cerebral cortex (10). Thus, mineralocorticoids coupled with increased neuronal activity might be the main stimulus enhancing the expression of the NGF gene in the hippocampus.

NGF has been shown to rescue lesion-induced degeneration of cholinergic neurons of the basal forebrain (11,12). These data suggest that NGF can be an important component in therapy to stimulate and perhaps accelerate CNS repair. Neurotrophic action of glucocorticoids has been shown as well. In fact, in adrenalectomized rats, changes in cell morphology as well as death of a large number of hippocampal neurons were significantly reduced by the administration of corticosterone (8). Some neuronal populations thus appear to require glucocorticoids to regulate various factors essential for survival and maintenance of their normal morphology (8). However, the question remains whether glucocorticoids may have a direct trophic action. In fact, glucocorticoids modulate the gene expression of several brain proteins (13) which can be important in triggering neuronal trophism. For instance, corticosterone regulates the gene expression of calbindin, a neuronal specific Ca^{2+} binding protein, in the CA1 area and dentate nucleus of the rat hippocampus (14). The trophic role of intracellular Ca^{2+} is now well established. Changes in Ca^{2+} concentration are crucial in axonal transport, in releasing transmitters and in signal transduction.

Our data that indicate that adrenal steroids might function as regulatory stimuli in the modulation of cortical NGF expression, support the possibility that NGF represents a link whereby the adrenal cortical system can exert a trophic action in the CNS (15). Moreover, the increase in NGF biosynthesis induced by steroids or bicuculline may represent one of the molecular events whereby the organism returns to its original homeostasis after a stress response, or may represent the trigger for important functional changes related to adaptation. These hypotheses broad the spectrum of action of NGF in the CNS and open new possibilities for an understanding of the physiological role of this neurotrophic molecule.

References

1. McEwen BS, De Kloet ER, Rostene W. Adrenal steroid receptors and action in the nervous system. *Physiol Rev* 1986;66:1121–1188.
2. Aloe L. Adrenalectomy decreases nerve growth factor in young adult rat hippocampus. *Proc Natl Acad Sci USA* 1989;86:5636–5640.
3. Fabrazzo M, Costa E, Mocchetti I. Stimulation of nerve growth factor biosynthesis in developing rat brain by reserpine: steroids as potential mediators. *Mol Pharmacol* 1991;39:144–149.
4. Sapolsky RM, Krey LC, McEwen BS. The neuroendocrinology of stress and aging: the glucocorticoid cascade hypothesis. *Endocrinol Rev* 1986;7:284–301.
5. Maickel RP, Westermann EO, Brodie BB. Effect of reserpine and cold-exposure on pituitary-adrenocortical function in rats. *J Pharmacol Exp Ther* 1961;134:167–172.
6. Westermann EO, Maickel RP, Brodie BB. On the mechanism of pituitary-adrenal stimulation by reserpine. *J Pharmacol Exp Ther* 1962;138:208–217.
7. Danielson PE, Forss-Petter S, Brown MA, et al. p1B15: A rat cDNA clone encoding cyclophilin. *DNA* 1988;4:261–267.
8. Gould E, Woolley CS, McEwen BS. Short term glucocorticoid manipulation affects neuronal morphology and survival in the adult dentate gyrus. *Neuroscience* 1990;37:367–375.
9. Gall CM, Isackson PJ. Limbic seizure increases neuronal production of messenger RNA for nerve growth factor. *Science* 1989;245:758–761.
10. Chao HM, Choo PH, McEwen BS. Glucocorticoid and mineralocorticoid receptor mRNA expression in rat brain. *Neuroendocrinology* 1989;50:365–371.
11. Hefti F. Nerve growth factor promotes survival of septal cholinergic neurons after fimbrial transections. *J Neurosci* 1986;6:2155–2162.
12. Williams LR, Varon S, Peterson GM, et al. Continuous infusion of nerve growth factor prevents basal forebrain neuronal death after fimbria fornix transection. *Proc Natl Acad Sci USA* 1986;83:9231–9235.
13. Harlan RE. Regulation of neuropeptide gene expression by steroid hormones. *Mol Neurobiol* 1988;2:183–200.
14. Iacopino AM, Christakos S. Corticosterone regulates calbindin-D_{28k} mRNA and protein levels in rat hippocampus. *J Biol Chem* 1990;265:10177–10180.

15. Levi-Montalcini R, Aloe L, Alleva E. A role for nerve growth factor in nervous, endocrine and immune systems. *Prog NeuroEndocrinImmunol* 1990;3:1–10.

16. Dal Toso R, De Bernardi MA, Brooker G, et al. Beta-adrenergic and prostaglandin activation increases Nerve Growth Factor mRNA content in C6–2B rat astrocytoma cells. *J Pharmacol Exp Ther* 1988;246:1190–1193.

Glucocorticoids, Neurotoxicity and Calcium Regulation

E. Elliott and R. Sapolsky, Ph.D.

*Department of Biological Sciences, Stanford University,
Stanford, California 94305*

During stress, enhanced activity of the hypothalamic-pituitary-adrenal axis results in an elevation of circulating glucocorticoids (GCs) (1). A major target in the brain for these hormones is the hippocampus (2). With excessive exposure to GCs (during chronic stress, aging or GC administration), hippocampal neurons can degenerate (3–5). This action is apparent in rats and primates (6). GC-induced hippocampal neurotoxicity can be decelerated by decreasing GC exposure either surgically (4) or behaviorally (7).

Even more alarming, exposure of the hippocampus to elevated (but not neurotoxic) GC concentrations increases the toxicity of various insults including hypoxia–ischemia, excitotoxic seizures, hypoglycemia, antimetabolites and oxygen radical generators (cf. 8). For example, rats with high physiological levels of GCs have increased hippocampal damage after administration of kainic acid (KA; a glutamatergic excitotoxin that produces seizures) relative to control rats (9). Critically, no potentiation of toxicity occurs in brain regions sensitive to KA but lacking high concentrations of receptors for GCs. Conversely, the reduction of GC concentrations protects the hippocampus from the extrinsic insults (10–12). In vitro studies with hippocampal cultures show that GCs exacerbate the toxicity of insults to both neurons and glia (13–15).

This GC endangerment of the hippocampus appears energetic in nature. As evidence, this endangerment can be attenuated in vivo and in vitro with supplementation of energy substrates (e.g., glucose, mannose and ketones) without affecting the damage induced by the toxin alone (13,16). As a possible route by which GCs induce this energetic vulnerabil-

47

ity, the hormones inhibit glucose transport 30% in hippocampal neurons and glia (14,17–19). This process is similar to the classic GC inhibition of glucose transport in numerous peripheral tissues (20). In vitro work has shown that the GC-induced impairment of glucose transport is not induced by other steroids (e.g., testosterone, estrogen or progesterone) and is not induced in cortical or hypothalamic cultures. Furthermore, the inhibition of transport is dose- and time-dependent and mediated by the Type II corticosteroid receptor (14,19). The GC-induced impairment of glucose transport could (along with other, as yet unrecognized catabolic GC actions in the hippocampus) induce a state of metabolic vulnerability, thus compromising the ability of hippocampal neurons to survive various coincident neurological insults. In fact, during energetic crises, GCs accelerate the decline in ATP content in cultured hippocampal glia and decrease the glycogen content in the hippocampus (in vivo) and in cultured glia (G. Tombaugh, manuscript in preparation).

Glucocorticoids and the Glutamate/N-Methyl-D-aspartate/Calcium Cascade

The energy requirement of hippocampal neurons is immense such that a 30% decrease in glucose transport (as induced by GCs) may be compromising energetically. Large quantities of energy are necessary for the maintenance and restoration of ionic gradients, maintenance of membrane structure, transport of material, and neurotransmission (21). Additionally, neurons can use only a few energy substrates and have a limited glycogen storage capacity (22). In fact, ischemia, hypoglycemia and epilepsy all appear to damage hippocampal neurons through an energy-dependent stereotypical cascade of dysregulation (23). Our recent work suggests that GCs exacerbate the toxicity of these insults by energetically exacerbating this cascade.

As will be familiar to most readers, the major hippocampal neurotransmitter implicated in these insults is the excitatory amino acid L-glutamate (or an analogue). Energy depletion exacerbates and initiates a cascade of excessive glutamate which, through enhanced activation of the N-methyl-D-aspartate (NMDA) receptor, leads to pathological excesses of cytosolic free calcium ($[Ca^{2+}]_i$) (cf. 24). A reduction in energy weakens neuronal ionic gradients, causes depolarization and results in excessive synaptic glutamate release and diminished reuptake. This abnormal activity results in increased calcium influx through voltage-gated calcium channels (VOCs), removal of the magnesium blockade of the NMDA receptor–gated calcium channel, and (due to energy depletion) disrupted calcium sequestration and efflux (25,26). The net result of this cascade is an abnormal sustained elevation of $[Ca^{2+}]_i$, which can activate catabolic enzymes that in turn cause membrane and neurofilament degradation and subsequent neurotoxicity (24,27).

The energy-dependent GC-induced endangerment also may result from an exacerbation of the glutamate/NMDA/calcium cascade. As evidence, GCs inhibit both glial glutamate uptake and a component of $[^3H]$glutamate binding thought to represent neuronal reuptake, thus allowing glutamate to persist in the synapse (14,28). This effect is energy-dependent in that the GC inhibition of glial glutamate uptake is eliminated with energy supplementation and mimicked by energy deprivation (14). Additionally, GCs, in an energy-dependent manner, enhance the extracellular accumulation of glutamate after KA exposure, as assessed by in vivo microdialysis (29). Furthermore, the GC endangerment is eliminated with an NMDA receptor antagonist (30). Whether GCs disrupt other means of glutamate regulation is unknown. (However, GC stimulation of glutamine synthetase, which could exacerbate the glutamate/NMDA/calcium cascade, has been shown not to be associated with the GC-induced neurotoxicity [31].)

Glucocorticoids and Neuronal Calcium Regulation

Thus, GCs disrupt hippocampal neuronal glutamate regulation in an energy-dependent manner. An end result of the glutamate/NMDA/calcium cascade is the prolonged elevation of neuronal $[Ca^{2+}]_i$. Therefore, to implicate further the glutamate/NMDA/calcium cascade as a mechanism of the GC-induced endangerment, we investigated the effects of GCs on hippocampal neuronal calcium regulation. Fluorescent calcium probes (fura-2 and fluo-3) were used because they offer the least biologically disruptive mechanisms of $[Ca^{2+}]_i$ measurement, while providing excellent spatial and temporal resolution.

Primary cultures of fetal rat hippocampal neurons and glia were treated with GCs for 24 hr. GC treatment caused a 45% increase in neuronal basal $[Ca^{2+}]_i$ (E. Elliott et al., manuscript in preparation). We then exposed each neuron to an energetic insult, 100 μM KA for 300 sec (32). GC treatment caused a 23-fold increase in the magnitude of the $[Ca^{2+}]_i$ response to KA, a sevenfold increase in the peak magnitude of the $[Ca^{2+}]_i$ response, and a twofold increase in $[Ca^{2+}]_i$ recovery time. Glucose supplementation reduced the GC effect on the magnitude and peak magnitude of the $[Ca^{2+}]_i$ response to KA. Glucose reduction (by 30%, the same magnitude that GCs decrease hippocampal neuronal glucose transport) mimicked the GC effect on the peak magnitude of the $[Ca^{2+}]_i$ response to KA. Thus, GCs increase hippocampal neuronal basal and stimulated $[Ca^{2+}]_i$ in an energy-dependent manner.

We next investigated whether the GC effect on neuronal calcium regulation arose from an effect on basal calcium influx and/or stimulated calcium efflux. During basal conditions the neuronal calcium gradient is inward; thus, on removal of extracellular calcium the decline of basal calcium represents the previous contribution of calcium influx. In contrast, during stimulated conditions the neuronal calcium gradient is outward; thus, after potassium-induced stimulation, the decline of neuronal calcium represents calcium efflux. Using this protocol, we found that GCs reduce hippocampal neuronal calcium efflux after potassium stimulation (E. Elliott et al., manuscript in preparation). This result helps explain the GC enhancement of KA-induced calcium elevation. Other studies suggest an effect of GCs on calcium influx through VOCs. GCs increase calcium-dependent afterhyperpolarizations and relatively "pure" calcium action potentials in the hippocampus (33,34). Energy depletion, due to GC exposure, could weaken neuronal ionic gradients, cause depolarization and thus enhance calcium influx through VOCs.

Regardless of the mechanism of the GC-induced increase in basal and stimulated $[Ca^{2+}]_i$, a prolonged elevation of $[Ca^{2+}]_i$ can activate calcium-dependent enzymes which can degrade the neuronal cytoskeleton. For example, hippocampal neurons contain high levels of the protease calpain I, which undergoes autoproteolytic activation in the presence of an elevated concentration of free calcium (35,36). Spectrin is the preferred substrate of calpain I and a major component of the neuronal cytoskeleton (37). Excessive degradation of spectrin would be expected to disrupt intracellular transport and membrane-related functions vital to the continued stability of dendritic and axonal processes (38). In fact, hippocampal neurons exposed to glutamate exhibit spectrin breakdown, which correlates well with subsequent neuronal degeneration (27,39).

One prediction stemming from the GC-induced elevation of neuronal basal and stimulated $[Ca^{2+}]_i$ is that GCs would increase the KA-induced activation of calcium-dependent calpain I and thus increase spectrin breakdown. Evidence supports this prediction; after hippocampal KA microinfusion, GC-treated rats have more than double the spectrin breakdown than do control rats, and this GC effect is eliminated by energy supplementation (40).

GCs affect another aspect of calcium-dependent enzyme activation, phosphorylation and abnormal accumulation of the tau protein. Tau, localized in neuronal axons, promotes the polymerization of tubulin into microtubules (which determine neuronal shape and are required for fast axonal transport) and stabilizes these fibrous organelles. Tau is abnormally altered (possibly phosphorylated) in Alzheimer's disease and other neurological diseases (41,42). This altered tau (along with other cytoskeletal proteins and referred to as neurofibrillary tangles) accumulates within neurons and is incapable of microtubule assembly. Because of the instability of the microtubules, neuronal degeneration can occur.

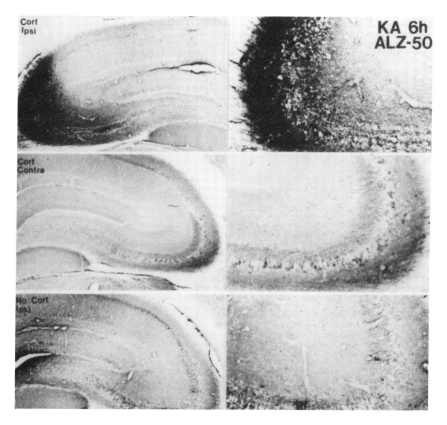

Figure 1. ALZ-50 immunoreactivity in Ammon's horn of the hippocampus 6 hr after unilateral kainic acid (KA) microinfusion. **Top**: Corticosterone(Cort)-treated rats, from the KA-infused side, low and high magnification. **Middle**: Cort-treated rats, from the side contralateral (Contra) to the KA infusion. **Bottom**: Adrenalectomized rats, from the KA-infused side. Ipsi, ipsilateral. (From E. Elliott, M. Mattson and R. Sapolsky, manuscript in preparation.)

Another prediction stemming from the GC-induced elevation of neuronal basal and stimulated $[Ca^{2+}]_i$ is that GCs increase the accumulation of abnormally altered tau and that this increase correlates with subsequent neurotoxicity. Our recent findings support this concept; after KA microinfusion, GC-treated rats have more phosphorylation-dependent tau immunoreactivity than do control rats (Figure 1; E. Elliott et al., manuscript in preparation). Additionally, this tau immunoreactivity and subsequent neurotoxicity (measured by Nissl stain) are found in the CA3 region of the hippocampus, the region most sensitive to KA-induced neurotoxicity. This finding lends further support that the GCs are not directly neurotoxic but rather increase the toxicity of other energetic insults.

Conclusions

Prolonged exposure to GCs, for example during chronic stress, aging or GC administration, can cause hippocampal neurotoxicity. Furthermore, acute GC exposure can cause hippocampal neuronal vulnerability to extrinsic energetic insults. This endangerment appears metabolic; the mechanism is possibly a reduction in hippocampal neuronal and glial glucose transport. This GC-induced energy depletion exacerbates or initiates the glutamate/NMDA/calcium cascade evident in hippocampal neurons during other energetic insults. A consequence of this cascade is the prolonged elevation of $[Ca^{2+}]_i$. The GC-induced basal and stimulated neuronal calcium elevation activates catabolic enzymes and causes abnormal cytoskeletal accumulations associated with later neurotoxicity.

Acknowledgment

Studies were supported by grant NIH RO1 AG06633 to R.M.S.

References

1.   Dallman M, Akana S, Cascio C, et al. Regulation of ACTH secretion: variations on a theme of B. *Recent Prog Horm Res* 1987;43:113–173.

2.   McEwen B, de Kloet E, Rostene W. Adrenal steroid receptors and actions in the nervous system. *Physiol Rev* 1986;66:1121–1188.

3.   Aus der Muhlen D, Ockenfels H. Morphologische Veranderungen in Diencephalon und Telencephalon nach Storgen des Regelkreises Adenohypophysenebennierenrinde. III. Ergebnisee beim Meerschweinchen nach Verabrerichung von Cortison und Hydrocortison. *Z Zellforsch* 1969;56:395–433.

4. Landfield P, Baskin R, Pitler T. Brain aging correlates: retardation by hormonal-pharmacological treatments. *Science* 1981;214:581–584.

5. Sapolsky R, Krey L, McEwen B. Prolonged glucocorticoid exposure reduces hippocampal neuron number: implications for aging. *J Neurosci* 1985;5:1221–1226.

6. Sapolsky R, Uno H, Rebert C, et al. Hippocampal damage associated with prolonged glucocorticoid exposure in primates. *J Neurosci* 1990;10:2897–2902.

7. Meaney M, Aitken D, Bhatnager S, et al. Effect of neonatal handling on age-related impairments associated with the hippocampus. *Science* 1988;239:766–769.

8. Sapolsky R. Glucocorticoids, hippocampal damage and the glutamatergic synapse. *Prog Brain Res* 1990;86:13–23.

9. Sapolsky R. A mechanism for glucocorticoid toxicity in the hippocampus: increased neuronal vulnerability to metabolic insults. *J Neurosci* 1985;5:1228-1232.

10. Sapolsky R, Pulsinelli W. Glucocorticoids potentiate ischemic injury to neurons: therapeutic implications. *Science* 1985;229:1397–1399.

11. Stein B, Sapolsky R. Chemical adrenalectomy reduces hippocampal damage induced by kainic acid. *Brain Res* 1988;473:175–180.

12. Morse J, Davis J. Regulation of ischemic hippocampal damage in the gerbil: adrenalectomy alters the rate of CA1 cell disappearance. *Exp Neurol* 1990; 110:86–94.

13. Sapolsky R, Packan D, Vale W. Glucocorticoid toxicity in the hippocampus: *in vitro* demonstration. *Brain Res* 1988;453:367–371.

14. Virgin C, Ha T, Packan D, et al. Glucocorticoids inhibit glucose transport and glutamate uptake in hippocampal astrocytes: implications for glucocorticoid neurotoxicity. *J Neurochem* 1991;(in press).

15. Tombaugh GC, Sapolsky RM. Corticosterone exacerbates ischemic-like injury in mixed hippocampal cultures. *Soc Neurosci Abstr* 1990;16:935.

16. Sapolsky R. Glucocorticoid toxicity in the hippocampus: reversal by supplementation with brain fuels. *J Neurosci* 1986;6:2240–2246.

17. Phillips P, Berger C, Rottenberg D. High-dose dexamethasone decreases regional cerebral glucose metabolism in the rat. *Neurology* 1987;37(Suppl 1):Abstr 248.

18. Kadekaro M, Ito M, Gross P, et al. Local cerebral glucose utilization is increased in acutely adrenalectomized rats. *Neuroendocrinology* 1988;47:329–334.

19. Horner H, Packan D, Sapolsky R. Glucocorticoids inhibit glucose transport in cultured hippocampal neurons and glia. *Neuroendocrinology* 1990;52:57–64.

20. Munck A. Glucocorticoid inhibition of glucose uptake by peripheral tissues: old and new evidence, molecular mechanisms and physiological significance. *Perspect Biol Med* 1971;14:265–281.

21. Siesjo B. Cerebral circulation and metabolism. *J Neurosurg* 1984;60:883–908.

22. Siesjo B. Historical overview: calcium, ischemia and death of brain cells. *Ann NY Acad Sci* 1988;522:638–661.

23. Auer R, Siesjo B. Biological differences between ischemia, hypoglycemia, and epilepsy. *Ann Neurol* 1988;24:699–714.

24. Choi D. Glutamate neurotoxicity and diseases of the nervous system. *Neuron* 1988;1:623–634.

25. Cox J, Lysko P, Henneberry R. Excitatory amino acid neurotoxicity at the *N*-methyl-D-aspartate receptor in cultured neurons: role of the voltage-dependent magnesium block. *Brain Res* 1989;499:267–272.

26. Gibson G, Manger T, Toral-Barza L, et al. Cytosolic-free calcium and neurotransmitter release with decreased availability of glucose or oxygen. *Neurochem Res* 1989;14:437–443.

27. Simon R, Noszek J. Excitatory amino acids activate calpain I and induce structural protein breakdown *in vivo*. *Neuron* 1988;1:279–287.

28. Halpain S, McEwen B. Corticosterone decreases ^{3}H-glutamate binding in rat hippocampal formation. *Neuroendocrinology* 1988;48:235–241.

29. Stein-Behrens B, Elliott E, Miller C, et al. Glucocorticoids exacerbate kainic acid-induced extracellular accumulation of excitatory amino acids in the rat hippocampus. Submitted.

30. Armanini M, Hutchins C, Stein B, et al. Glucocorticoid endangerment of hippocampal neurons is NMDA-receptor dependent. *Brain Res* 1990;532:7–14.

31. Tombaugh G, Sapolsky R. Hippocampal glutamine synthetase: insensitivity to glucocorticoids and stress. *Am J Physiol* 1990;258:E894–E897.

32. Elliott E, Chang I, Sapolsky R. Corticosterone enhances kainic acid-induced calcium mobilization in cultured hippocampal neurons. *Soc Neurosci Abstr* 1990;16:171.

33. Joels M, de Kloet E. Effects of glucocorticoids and norepinephrine on the excitability in the hippocampus. *Science* 1989;245:1502–1505.

34. Kerr D, Campbell L, Hao S, et al. Corticosteroid modulation of hippocampal potentials: increased effect with aging. *Science* 1989;245:1505–1509.

35. Siman R, Gall C, Perlmutter L, et al. Distribution of calpain I, an enzyme associated with degenerative activity, in rat brain. *Brain Res* 1985;347:399–403.

36. Suzuki K, Imajoh S, Emori Y, et al. Calcium-activated neutral protease and its endogenous inhibitor. *FEBS Lett* 1987;220:271–277.

37. Levine J, Willard M. Fodrin: axonally transported polypeptides associated with the internal periphery of many cells. *J Cell Biol* 1981;90:631–643.

38. Seubert P, Lee K, Lynch G. Ischemia triggers NMDA receptor-linked cytoskeletal proteolysis in hippocampus. *Brain Res* 1989;492:366–370.

39. Simon R, Noszek J, Kegerise C. Calpain I activation is specifically related to excitatory amino acid induction of hippocampal damage. *J Neurosci* 1989;9:1579–1590.

40. Elliott E, Vanderklish P, Chang I, et al. Corticosterone exacerbates hippocampal calcium-dependent spectrin proteolysis *in vivo*. *Soc Neurosci Abstr* 1991;(in press).

41. Selkoe D. Biochemistry of altered brain proteins in Alzheimer's disease. *Annu Rev Neurosci* 1989;12:463–490.

42. Mattson M. Antigenic changes similar to those seen in neurofibrillary tangles are elicited by glutamate and Ca^{2+} influx in cultured hippocampal neurons. *Neuron* 1990;2:105–117.

Neuroprotectant Effects of Methylprednisolone and the 21-Aminosteroids

Edward D. Hall, Ph.D.

CNS Diseases Research, The Upjohn Company, Kalamazoo, Michigan 49001

We have systematically examined the efficacy of glucocorticoid steroids in experimental CNS trauma, using methylprednisolone (MP) as a prototype. Our primary mechanistic focus has been based on the hypothesis that the principal molecular basis for secondary posttraumatic neuronal degeneration is progressive membrane lipid peroxidation (LP) induced by oxygen free radicals (1,2). In our studies, the ability of MP to inhibit CNS-tissue LP was shown to be strongly correlated with the positive effects on other pathophysiologic processes and neurologic recovery. Separation of the anti-LP (i.e., antioxidant) and cerebroprotective effects from glucocorticoid activity has been achieved with the recent discovery of nonglucocorticoid steroids that duplicate or surpass the antioxidant effects of MP.

Our major effort has been to define the neuroprotective pharmacology of MP in spinal cord injury (3,4). We found that 30 mg/kg MP given intravenously to cats soon after blunt spinal cord injury could attenuate posttraumatic LP, as measured by various biochemical indices. In addition, extensive research has shown that the same dose of MP has other beneficial effects (many of which may be secondary to LP inhibition) on the injured spinal cord. These effects include the support of energy metabolism, prevention of progressive posttraumatic ischemia and neurofilament degradation, reversal of intracellular calcium accumulation, and inhibition of vasoactive prostaglandin $F_{2\alpha}$ and thromboxane A_2 formation. A 30 mg/kg dose of MP also may enhance the acute recovery of somatosensory evoked potentials; an increase in spinal neuronal excitability, another steroid effect, may be involved in neurophysiologic recovery.

Four observations describe the action of MP in spinal cord injury. First, large intravenous doses of MP are necessary, as described in the text above. Second is the complex, biphasic dose-response curve seen for many beneficial effects of MP. Although an intravenous 30 mg/kg dose is required to inhibit LP, doubling the dose causes a loss of that action. The logical explanation for such a pattern is that the high-dose pharmacology of MP is mediated by a direct membrane action.

Third, treatment must be initiated early to achieve a therapeutic effect. The uptake of MP by spinal tissue decreases rapidly after injury, probably because of secondary posttraumatic tissue loss and a progressive decrease in blood flow to the injury site. More importantly, however, LP-mediated tissue degeneration evolves rapidly after injury and is predominantly irreversible.

Fourth, the time course of MP's protective effects parallels the tissue uptake and elimination of the steroid. Because the half-life of MP in cat spinal tissue is only 2 to 6 hr, frequent doses are necessary to maintain blood flow, improve tissue preservation and maximize the potential for recovery. To demonstrate this concept, we designed and tested an intravenous dosing regimen in cats with moderately severe spinal injury (5). An initial 30 mg/kg bolus was given 30 min after injury, followed by 15 mg/kg doses 2 and 6 hr later, and then by continuous infusion of 2.5 mg/kg/hr for the remainder of the first 48 hr after injury. The cats were evaluated blindly for 4 weeks for their ability to walk, run and climb stairs. The cats then were sacrificed and a histologic analysis of the injury site was conducted.

In comparison with vehicle-treated animals, MP-treated cats showed significantly higher recovery scores beginning at 2 weeks after injury. In addition, a dramatic reduction in posttraumatic spinal tissue loss was observed, the degree of which was inversely correlated with the neurologic recovery score (r = –0.88). These studies clearly demonstrate that a dosing regimen centered on an inhibition of posttraumatic LP is associated with enhanced tissue preservation and functional recovery.

The recently published multicenter National Acute Spinal Cord Injury Study clinical trial (NASCIS II) shows that a similar MP dosing regimen administered within 8 hr after spinal cord injury can improve neurologic recovery in humans (6). Furthermore, the beneficial effect of antioxidant doses of MP supports the view that posttraumatic LP is a critical degenerative mechanism that can be effectively interrupted with antioxidant agents.

21-Aminosteroids

The definition of this high-dose nonglucocorticoid antioxidant action of MP led to the pursuit of nonglucocorticoid steroid analogs of MP (e.g., U-72099E), which also weakly inhibited LP in high concentrations and at high doses were active in models of experimental CNS trauma (7). However, efforts continued for the preparation of synthetic compounds that were even more potent and effective inhibitors of LP, with greater activity in experimental models of CNS trauma and ischemia. Such efforts resulted in the discovery of the 21-aminosteroids (such as U-74006F and U-74500A).

U-74006F (tirilazad mesylate) was selected for clinical development for the acute treatment of brain and spinal injury, subarachnoid hemorrhage, and stroke. Phase II clinical trials are ongoing for each of those indications. U-74500A, a more potent inhibitor of iron-catalyzed LP than U-74006F, has not been chosen for development because of pharmaceutical instability and rapid elimination in vivo.

Antioxidant Mechanisms

The 21-aminosteroids are potent inhibitors of LP in vitro. Using rat brain homogenates or purified rat brain synaptosomes as the lipid source, U-74006F and U-74500A potently inhibit iron-dependent LP, with an efficacy greatly surpassing that of the glucocorticoid steroid MP or the earlier-mentioned nonglucocorticoids such as U-72099E (8,9). Further, these 21-aminosteroids were found to decrease iron-induced damage to cultured cortical neurons (10).

Although the 21-aminosteroids are potent inhibitors of iron-dependent LP in intact phospholipid environments, they also inhibit LP in systems that do not contain membranes and which are free of iron. By using the free radical generator 2,2'-azobis(2,4-dimethyl valeronitrile) to initiate LP in a homogeneous methanol solution of linoleic acid, the 21-aminosteroids were found to inhibit LP by scavenging lipid peroxyl radicals (LOO$^\bullet$) and thus to block lipid radical chain reactions in a manner similar to vitamin E (11). The LOO$^\bullet$ scavenging action of the 21-aminosteroids resides in the amine portion of the molecule, and yields an as yet uncharacterized product. During the inhibition of LP, the 21-aminosteroids compete for the same reaction as vitamin E and slow its degradation (11). In vivo studies have demonstrated that U-74006F indeed preserves tissue vitamin E levels in the injured cat spinal cord (12).

In addition to scavenging LOO$^\bullet$, U-74006F also reacts with hydroxyl radicals generated during in vitro Fenton reactions (i.e., $Fe^{++} + H_2O_2 \rightarrow Fe^{+++} OH^- + \bullet OH$). Recently, data obtained from rodent models of head trauma and global ischemia have suggested that U-74006F also reduces hydroxyl radical concentration in vivo. Administration of salicylate, a hydroxyl radical trap, leads to the posttraumatic or postischemic formation of dihydroxybenzoic acid (DHBA) in brain tissue when DHBA reacts with a hydroxyl radical. U-74006F dosing leads to a decrease in DHBA formation, implying either a decreased formation or a scavenging of hydroxyl radicals (E.D. Hall et al., unpublished data).

U-74006F and U-74500A also have stabilizing effects on cell membranes. The release of free arachidonic acid from injured cell membranes is blocked by compounds in this series (13). This effect is not because of glucocorticoid activity of the compounds (i.e., phospholipase A_2 inhibition), but may be related to their antioxidant actions. In other studies, using cultured bovine brain microvascular endothelial cells, U-74006F and U-74500A localized within the hydrophobic core of cell membranes and caused an increase in lipid ordering (i.e., decreased fluidity) of the phospholipid bilayer (14). This action may help inhibit the propagation of LP by restricting the movement of LOO$^\bullet$ and alkoxyl radicals within the membrane.

Concerning other possible cerebroprotective mechanisms of action, neither U-74500A nor U-74006F produces hypothermic or CNS depressant effects (E.D. Hall et al., unpublished data) and they do not directly antagonize excitatory amino acid–induced neurotoxicity in vitro (i.e., they do not interact with N-methyl-D-aspartate receptors) (10). Moreover, neither U-74500A nor U-74006F exhibits any significant competition for cholinergic, adrenergic, serotonergic, dopaminergic, opiate or benzodiazepine receptors with standard ligands (E.D. Hall et al., unpublished data). Thus, the only demonstrated cerebroprotective mechanism of the 21-aminosteroids concerns their ability to block oxygen radical–induced LP.

Effects in Models of Spinal Cord Injury

U-74006F also has been investigated for its ability to promote neurologic recovery of cats after a moderately severe compression injury to the lumbar spinal cord (15). From 30 min after injury, the animals received a 48-hr intravenous regimen of vehicle (sterile water) or U-74006F in a random, blinded protocol similar to that employed in earlier studies with MP (3–5). Initial U-74006F doses ranged from 0.01 to 30 mg/kg. At 4 weeks after injury, vehicle-treated animals uniformly remained paraplegic. In contrast, cats that received 48-hr doses of U-74006F ranging from 1.6 to 160.0 mg/kg showed significantly better recovery, regaining approximately 75% of normal neurologic function. Histologic examination of the injured spinal cord segment showed a modest but statistically significant correlation (r = –0.57, p < 0.001) between cross-sectional tissue preservation and neurologic recovery score, indicating an effect of U-74006F in retarding posttraumatic tissue degeneration.

To pursue a mechanism by which U-74006F may promote chronic recovery after blunt spinal cord injury, the acute effects of U-74006F have also been examined in relation to a possible action to attenuate progressive posttraumatic spinal cord ischemia after moderately severe compression injury (12). In vehicle-treated cats, spinal cord blood flow (SCBF) progressively declined from normal levels immediately after injury, over the course of the experiment. By 4 hr postinjury, SCBF decreased 42%. In contrast, the 4-hr SCBF in cats treated with any of the three highest dose levels of U-74006F was significantly improved compared with the vehicle-treated cats. The molecular mechanism of action of U-74006F in antagonizing posttraumatic ischemia development may involve an inhibition of oxygen radical–mediated microvascular LP. This conclusion is based on the known involvement of LP in posttraumatic ischemia development (16) and the concomitant action of U-74006F in attenuating an injury-induced decline in spinal tissue vitamin E at the same doses that reduce posttraumatic ischemia (12).

Recent studies suggest that U-74006F retains its efficacy in promoting posttraumatic recovery after experimental spinal cord injury, even when initiation of treatment is delayed to 4 hr (17). Thus, this novel non-glucocorticoid 21-aminosteroid antioxidant shows considerable promise as a safer and possibly more effective acute treatment of spinal cord injury than MP.

References

1. Braughler JM, Hall ED. Central nervous system trauma and stroke: I. biochemical considerations for oxygen radical formation and lipid peroxidation. *Free Rad Biol Med* 1989;6:289–301.
2. Hall ED, Braughler JM. Central nervous system trauma and stroke: II. physiological and pharmacological evidence for the involvement of oxygen radicals and lipid peroxidation. *Free Rad Biol Med* 1989;6:303–313.
3. Hall ED, Braughler JM. Glucocorticoid mechanisms in spinal cord injury: a review and therapeutic rationale. *Surg Neurol* 1982;18:320–327.

4. Hall ED, Travis MA, Braughler JM. Pharmacological interventions in CNS ischemia and trauma: studies with high-dose methylprednisolone. In: Vincent JL, ed. *Update in intensive care and emergency medicine.* Berlin: Springer-Verlag, 1986;341–346.

5. Braughler JM, Hall ED, Means ED, et al. Evaluation of an intensive methylprednisolone sodium succinate dosing regimen in experimental spinal cord injury. *J Neurosurg* 1987;67:102–105.

6. Bracken MB, Shepard MJ, Collins WF, et al. A randomized controlled trial of methylprednisolone or naloxone in the treatment of acute spinal cord injury. *N Engl J Med* 1990;322:1405–1411.

7. Hall ED, McCall JM, Yonkers PA, et al. A non-glucocorticoid analog of methylprednisolone duplicates its high dose pharmacology in models of CNS trauma and neuronal membrane damage. *J Pharmacol Exp Ther* 1987;242:137–142.

8. Braughler JM, Pregenzer JF, Chase RL, et al. Novel 21-aminosteroids as potent inhibitors of iron-dependent lipid peroxidation. *J Biol Chem* 1987;262:10438–10440.

9. Hall ED, Yonkers PA, McCall JM, et al. Effect of the 21-aminosteroid U-74006F on experimental head injury in mice. *J Neurosurg* 1988;68:456–461.

10. Monyer H, Hartley DM, Choi DW. 21-Aminosteroids attenuate excitotoxic neuronal injury in cortical cell cultures. *Neuron* 1990;5:121–126.

11. Braughler JM, Pregenzer JF. The 21-aminosteroid inhibitors of lipid peroxidation: reactions with lipid peroxyl and phenoxyl radicals. *Free Rad Biol Med* 1989;7:125–130.

12. Hall ED, Yonkers PA, Horan KL, et al. Correlation between attenuation of posttraumatic spinal cord ischemia and preservation of vitamin E by the 21-aminosteroid U-74006F: evidence for an *in vivo* antioxidant action. *J Neurotrauma* 1989;6:169–176.

13. Braughler JM, Chase RL, Neff GL, et al. A new 21-aminosteroid antioxidant lacking glucocorticoid activity stimulates ACTH secretion and blocks arachidonic acid release from mouse pituitary tumor (AtT-20) cells. *J Pharmacol Exp Ther* 1988;244:423–427.

14. Audus KL, Guillot FL, Braughler JM. Evidence for 21-aminosteroid association with the hydrophobic domains of brain microvessel endothelial cells. *Free Rad Biol Med* 1991;(in press).

15. Anderson DK, Braughler JM, Hall ED, et al. Effects of treatment with U-74006F on neurological outcome following experimental spinal cord injury. *J Neurosurg* 1988;69:562–567.

16. Hall ED, Wolf DL. A pharmacological analysis of the pathophysiological mechanisms of post-traumatic spinal cord ischemia. *J Neurosurg* 1986;64:951–961.

17. Anderson DK, Hall ED, Braughler JM, et al. Effect of delayed administration of U74006F (tirilazad mesylate) on recovery of locomotor function following experimental spinal cord injury. *J Neurotrauma* 1991;(in press).

III

Plenary Lecture

Neurosteroids: A Function of the Brain

Etienne-Emile Baulieu, M.D., Ph.D.

Communications Hormonales (U 33) INSERM and Biochimie Hormonale, Faculté de Médecine Paris-Sud, 94275 Bicêtre Cedex, France

The relationship between steroids and cerebral function may be reconsidered in light of the recent discovery of a biosynthetic pathway of steroidal compounds ensuring the synthesis of "neurosteroids" (1) from cholesterol (C) in certain brain cells. Neurosteroids accumulate in the CNS independently of peripheral sources, which classically provide steroids to the brain.

The synthesis of gluco- and mineralocorticosteroids in the adrenal glands and that of sex steroids in the gonads and placenta stems from C. The lipophilic properties of steroids facilitate their easy passage through the blood-brain barrier in free form (that is, nonesterified and not bound to protein). At the cerebral level, the function of many nerve cells is influenced by steroid hormones originating from the periphery; the best known examples are neurons that secrete hypophysiotropic factors stimulating the production of pituitary hormones such as adrenocorticotropic hormone (ACTH) and gonadotropins which are subjected to regulation by the corresponding steroid hormones by a feedback mechanism. Mapping intracellular steroid receptors by autoradiography with radioactive hormones administered to the animal or incubated with brain tissue sections, and by immunohistochemistry using antireceptor antibodies has led to the identification of specific neuronal ensembles in the hypothalamus (for review see refs. 2 and 3). However, the mechanisms by which steroid hormones influence mental, behavioral and brain metabolic processes remain essentially unknown. Differentiating effects of testosterone (T) are mediated by its transformation to estrogens in the rat brain and its subsequent association with the relevant estrogen receptor, already indicating the critical importance of steroid metabolism in the CNS.

Cerebral Steroids Unexplained by Peripheral Gland Production

In the adrenals and gonads, pregnenolone (Δ5P)[1] is formed from C; its 21-carbon structure is the result of oxidative cleavage of the side chain in mitochondria. In turn, cleavage of the Δ5P side chain results in the formation of the C19-steroid dehydroepiandrosterone (DHA) (4). Δ5P and DHA conserve the Δ5–3β-hydroxylated structure of C.

We observed the presence of DHA (5) and Δ5P (6) in the rat brain at concentrations superior to those found in the blood, in contrast with corticosterone and T, the plasma levels of which are greatly superior to cerebral concentrations. Brain DHA is not affected by adrenal stimulation with ACTH or adrenal inhibition by dexamethasone. Cerebral Δ5P and DHA are subject to circadian fluctuations not in phase with those of adrenal steroids in the plasma. Δ5P is already present in the brain at high concentrations during the postnatal period, which in the rat is characterized by an almost complete inactivity of the adrenal glands. An indirectly related but nevertheless important finding to support the cerebral synthesis of neurosteroids is obtained after castration and adrenalectomy: cerebral Δ5P and DHA persist in the brain despite several weeks of peripheral hormone deficit, in contrast with T of testicular origin, which rapidly disappears after castration. Experiments in which, after intraperitoneal administration of radioactive Δ5P and DHA, rapid entry into and exit out of the cerebral compartment have been observed also suggest that accumulation of cerebral steroids does not depend simply on storage in the brain. Moreover, the use of aminoglutethimide, which inhibits the synthesis of Δ5P from C, causes a decline in the concentration of Δ5P in the brain. The cerebral clearance of neurosteroids seems quite rapid, implying a high renewal rate (7–9).

Δ5P and DHA are present in the brain in the form of nonconjugated steroids ("free"), sulfate esters (S), and fatty acid esters (lipoidal derivatives, L). The concentrations of these derivatives were measured in the young adult rat brain 10 hr after the beginning of illumination, close to the acrophase of circadian variations (10). The values corresponding to

---

[1]Nomenclature and abbreviations. We use definitions and abbreviations generally accepted by steroid biochemists. Reduced metabolites are indicated with specific reference to the position of the chemical groups indicated by the number of the involved carbon atom of the hormone. For example: the tetrahydrogenated derivative of P (3α-hydroxy,5α-pregnane-20-one) is 3α,5α-THP; the dihydrogenated derivative of Δ5P (20α-hydroxypregnenolone) is 20α-DH-Δ5P. Hydroxylations are referred to by OH: 7α-hydroxydehydroepiandrosterone is 7α-OH-DHA.

average concentrations in the brain are on the order of 10^{-8} and even 10^{-7} M, identical in males and females. Given the probable compartmentalization of steroid distribution, this result implies the existence of rather high local concentrations.

ng/g ± SD	P	PS	PL	DS	DL
Males	25 ± 8	19 ± 6	46 ± 14	2.1 ± 0.5	0.59 ± 0.30
Females	32 ± 15	19 ± 6	46 ± 19	1.7 ± 0.4	0.34 ± 0.12

Steroidogenesis by Oligodendrocytes and Neurosteroid Metabolism

The demonstration of Δ5P synthesis from C by a neural formation has proved difficult. Experiments using radioactive precursors in tissue sections, homogenates and subcellular fractions obtained from the whole brain of rats (and other animals) were negative. This result is probably due to several reasons, including cellular heterogeneity (supposing that the synthesis is limited to certain cells), the high level of endogenous C (diluting the radioactivity of the tracer-precursor intended to label Δ5P) and the difficult access of tracer amounts of precursor to the enzymes of steroidogenesis (partition in the lipids).

Although previous biochemical experiments failed, an immunohistochemical study designed to localize enzymes implicated in brain cell steroidogenesis was successful and led to the demonstration of the formation of Δ5P from C in rat oligodendrocytes (11–13). However, when we studied the metabolism of C-[^{3}H] under the same conditions in the mitochondria of whole brain, there was no apparent formation of Δ5P-[^{3}H], again indicating the difficulty of demonstrating the reaction. Recently, we confirmed by Western blot technique the presence of cytochrome P-450$_{scc}$ (scc, side-chain cleavage) in oligodendrocytes, which also was found in the mitochondria of brains from pregnant rats (14). Our results recently have been confirmed immunohistologically and biochemically by Iwahashi and colleagues (15).

Studies of various cell types in culture (as summarized in the chapter by Robel et al., *this volume*) indicate the following: 1) the presence and function of cytochrome P-450$_{scc}$ in oligodendrocytes; 2) the function of 3β-hydroxysteroid dehydrogenase in astrocytes, which can particularly ensure the formation of P from Δ5P; 3) the lack of cytochrome P-450$_{scc}$ and 3β-hydroxysteroid dehydrogenase in neurons we have studied; and 4) the presence of 5α-reductase and 3α- and 3β-hydroxysteroid oxidoreductases [which may transform P or 11-deoxycorticosterone (DOC) into 3α,5α-THP and 3α,5α-THDOC, respectively], and of 7α-hydroxylase of very high activity (Y. Akwa, unpublished data) and 20α-hydroxysteroid oxidoreductase in glial cells. However, the transformation of Δ5P to DHA has never been ascertained in any biopreparation of cerebral origin. Incidentally, we have not found any indication of the formation of T or (11β-hydroxylated) corticosteroids in brain cells.

In the peripheral nervous system, there may be formation of neurosteroids, as recently we identified Δ5P in relatively large amounts (approximately 40 ng/g) in human sciatic nerves (R. Morfin and J. Young, unpublished data).

Neurosteroids and Behavior

Several experiments have indicated the potential of DHA and Δ5P to interfere with behavioral phenomena. An antiaggressive effect of DHA has been demonstrated in castrated male mice that become aggressive in the presence of lactating females. This aggressiveness, absent in intact males, occurs in castrated animals and is suppressed by administration of T or estradiol (16). In collaboration (17), we have shown that small doses of DHA also can abolish the aggressiveness of castrated males. Because DHA can be metabolically transformed into T, although the quantities of this steroid found at the brain level were quite small, we used a derivative of DHA, 3β-methyl-Δ5-androstene-17-one, lacking hormonal action, to avoid any transformation into sex hormones. This compound had an inhibitory action on the aggressiveness at least equal to that of DHA, and thus may be a prototype for inhibitory steroids. Its mechanism of action may be indirect, because after administration of either DHA or 3β-methyl-Δ5-androstene-17-one (18) we observed a selective decrease of Δ5P-S, which is itself an antagonist of γ-aminobutyric acid$_A$ receptor (GABA$_A$R) function (see Mechanisms of Neurosteroid Action).

Δ5P is present in the olfactory bulb of male rats at a level higher than the cerebral mean concentration. Δ5P may be a link in the chain of events after heterosexual exposure of animals. In reference to values found in male rats exposed to the scent of other male rats, Δ5P levels selectively decrease in the olfactory bulbs of animals exposed to the scent of females in estrus (19). Such an odoriferous signal of females seems to require ovarian function, because it disappears after castration and is reestablished by estradiol administration. Moreover, not only was the concentration of Δ5P reduced in the olfactory bulb of castrated males, but the message-odor of females became ineffective in these animals, with no change of Δ5P concentration on exposure to females, whereas it was restored by administration of T (which cannot be transformed to Δ5P). It is rather remarkable that a pheromonal signal is perceived in a hormone-dependent manner.

Δ5P-S, present and biosynthesized in the CNS as indicated before, is an inhibitor of GABA$_A$R function. In addition to biochemical studies (20,21), Δ5P-S recently was demonstrated in vivo to decrease the sleeping time in rats anesthetized with a barbiturate after intraventricular (and even intraperitoneal) administration (22). Whether Δ5P-S and DHA-S, which both specifically bind to synaptosomes (M.J. Sancho, B. Eychenne and P. Robel, unpublished data), play a physiological role in the modulation of the GABA$_A$R cannot be excluded. Δ5P-S and DHA-S may be part of a modulatory steroidal system functioning in the brain (Figure 1). Rather old pharmacological experiments showed the sedative/anesthetic effects of some steroids (23–25), and one of these compounds was used long ago as adjuvant in general anesthesia. Recently, 3α,5α-THP and other reduced metabolites of progesterone (P) and DOC have been shown to potentiate GABA$_A$R activities (26), a mechanism that possibly explains the sleepiness of pregnant women or of patients treated with high doses of P. The physiological concentrations of reduced metabolites in the brain are largely unknown at present. Recently, we found large amounts of 3α,5α-THP in the brains of pregnant rats (approximately 30 ng/g).

Finally, DHA has been reported to have a trophic effect on mouse neurons in culture and also reinforces long-term memory of an active avoidance behavior (27). Preliminary findings indicate an effect of P on oligodendrocyte growth and differentiation in vitro (I. Jung-Testas, unpublished data).

Mechanisms of Neurosteroid Action

The intranuclear DNA binding receptors of steroid hormones are well known. At present there is no evidence for intracellular receptors of DHA or Δ5P or their esters. Considering that P may be synthesized by glial cells as a neurosteroid, the recent demonstration of an estrogen-induced P receptor in cultured oligodendrocytes of rats of both sexes (28) suggests a classical intracellular mechanism of action for neurosteroidal P, but in a paracrine or autocrine manner rather than endocrine arrangement. Incidentally, besides hypothalamic distribution, the P receptor also was found in the cerebral cortex (29) and meningiomas (30).

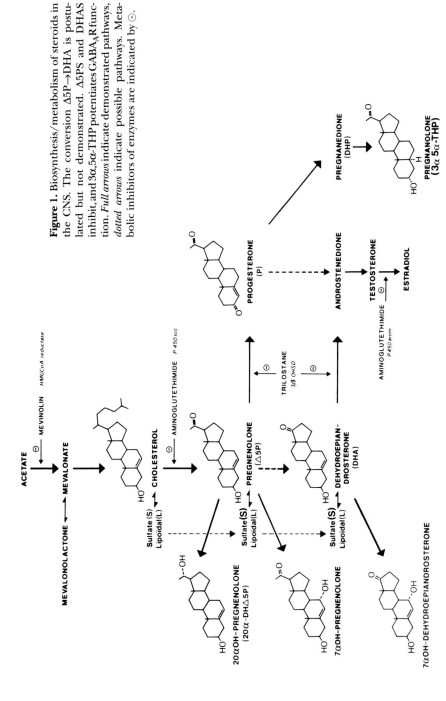

Figure 1. Biosynthesis/metabolism of steroids in the CNS. The conversion Δ5P→DHA is postulated but not demonstrated. Δ5PS and DHAS inhibit, and 3α,5α-THP potentiates GABA$_A$R function. *Full arrows* indicate demonstrated pathways, *dotted arrows* indicate possible pathways. Metabolic inhibitors of enzymes are indicated by ⊙.

However, a membrane mechanism of action of steroids cannot be excluded. The only precedent for the existence of a membrane receptor, including the demonstration of steroid binding and induced response, is the case of the *Xenopus* oocyte: P added to the incubation medium provokes the reinitiation of meiosis (31). Experiments with "macromolecular P" unable to enter the cells, and a photoaffinity labeling technique have permitted the characterization of a membrane binding protein of approximately 30 kD, with the properties of affinity and hormonal specificity of a receptor (32). The inhibitory effect of P on adenylate cyclase activity in the intact cells was reproduced in vitro with a membrane preparation (33). Steroid specificity, molecular weight, and mechanism of action are completely different when comparing P receptors and intracellular P receptors: they are distinct proteins. Other results with various cells suggest that steroid hormones, particularly estrogens, may act at the membrane level. These results are mostly from binding and electrophysiological studies (34–39). By acting on the neuronal membrane, steroids may rapidly modulate the release of neurotransmitters and the activity of membrane receptors and ion channels.

With neurosteroids, electrophysiological experiments in vivo have shown that DHA, DHA-S and Δ5P-S can selectively stimulate the electrical activity of individual neurons when introduced at their location in the antero-septal region of the guinea pig brain (40).

The molecular mechanism of the anesthetic effect of P-reduced metabolites calls on the $GABA_AR$ system. Several subunits of all $GABA_AR$ variants (41,42) demonstrate binding sites not only for GABA itself, but also, for example, for barbiturates, benzodiazepines, and convulsants. $3\alpha,5\alpha$-THP and other reduced P derivatives potentialize effects of GABA, apparently by interacting with site(s) probably different from those of other known ligands (43–45). In this volume, reports by several groups of investigators address this functional aspect of neurosteroid activity. In contrast, Δ5P-S and DHA-S act as antagonists and, like picrotoxin, block the effect of GABA on the chloride channel, reducing the frequency of openings in neurons in culture (20,21,46). Studies are underway to determine if these steroid effects are common to all $GABA_ARs$ in all cell types. Neurosteroid modulation of the $GABA_AR$ thus is a novel membrane effect of steroids. The apparent K_i of Δ5P-S and DHA-S in in vitro experiments is compatible with local concentrations that may be established by endogenous steroids. The concentration of $3\alpha,5\alpha$-THP in the brain (20 ng/g total brain) during pregnancy is largely sufficient to potentiate GABA agonist activity.

Whether the membrane effects of neurosteroids are mediated only by their interaction with binding sites of neurotransmitter receptors, or if neurosteroids also exert their action on specific membrane steroid receptors or even by their insertion into the proteolipidic composition of neuronal and glial plasma membranes remains to be elucidated (note that Δ5P and DHA have the same ring structure as C but, lacking the lipophilic side chain, may destabilize the membrane structure if replacing the sterol).

Data concerning the biosynthesis of steroids in the brain are probably applicable to the human. Neurosteroids have been measured at elevated concentrations in the brain of the cadaver (47,48) and the enzymes of the complex involved in side-chain cleavage of C have been demonstrated immunohistochemically (49). However, we are not yet close to medical applications.

Acknowledgments

This work was carried out in INSERM Unit 33, principally with my long-time colleague P. Robel, and with Y. Akwa, E. Bourreau, C. Clarke, C. Corpéchot, B. Eychenne, C. Le Goascogne, M. Gouézou, A. Groyer, Z.Y. Hu, D.H. Jo, K. Kabbadj, I. Jung-Testas, R. Morfin, M.J. Sancho, M. Synguelakis, S. Talha, O. Vatier, C. Vourc'h and J. Young, and also with the collaboration of M. Axelson (Stockholm), P. Brazeau (Montréal), F. Halberg (Minneapolis), M. Haug (Strasbourg), D.M. Majewska (Bethesda), I. Mason (Dallas), M.L. Schlegel (Strasbourg), J. Sjövall (Stockholm), R. Vihko (Oulu) and M. Waterman (Dallas). We thank Roussel-Uclaf, la Fondation Del Duca, the Florence Gould Foundation and l'Association Française de lutte contre les Myopathies (AFM) for their support.

References

1. Baulieu EE. Steroid hormones in the brain: several mechanisms? In: Fuxe K, Gustafsson JA, Wetterberg L, eds. *Steroid hormone regulation of the brain.* Oxford: Pergamon Press, 1981;3–14.

2. Celotti I, Massa R, Martini L. Metabolism of sex steroids in the central nervous system. In: De Groot LJ, Cahill GF, Steinberger E Jr, et al., eds. *Endocrinology,* vol 1. New York: Greene & Stratton, 1979;41–53.

3. Fuxe K, Gustafsson JA, Wetterberg L, eds. *Steroid hormone regulation of the brain.* Oxford: Pergamon Press, 1981.

4. Lieberman S, Greenfield MJ, Wolfson A. A heuristic proposal for understanding steroidogenic processes. *Endocr Rev* 1981;5:128–148.

5. Corpéchot C, Robel P, Axelson M, et al. Characterization and measurement of dehydroepiandrosterone sulfate in the rat brain. *Proc Natl Acad Sci USA* 1981; 78:4704–4707.

6. Corpéchot C, Synguelakis M, Talha S, et al. Pregnenolone and its sulfate ester in the rat brain. *Brain Res* 1983;270:119–125.

7. Baulieu EE, Robel P, Vatier O, et al. Neurosteroids: pregnenolone and dehydroepiandrosterone in the brain. In: Fuxe K, Agnati LF, eds. *Receptor-receptor interactions*, vol 48. Basingstoke: MacMillan Press, 1987;89–104.

8. Robel P, Baulieu EE. Neuro-steroids: 3β-hydroxy-Δ5-derivatives in the rodent brain. *Neurochem Int* 1985;7:953–958.

9. Robel P, Bourreau E, Corpéchot C, et al. Neuro-steroids: 3β-hydroxy-Δ5-derivatives in rat and monkey brain. *J Steroid Biochem* 1987;27:649–655.

10. Jo DH, Aït Abdallah M, Young J, et al. Pregnenolone, dehydroepiandrosterone, and their sulfate and fatty acid esters in the rat brain. *Steroids* 1989;54:287–297.

11. Le Goascogne C, Robel P, Gouézou M, et al. Neurosteroids: cytochrome P450$_{scc}$ in rat brain. *Science* 1987;237:1212–1215.

12. Jung-Testas I, Alliot F, Pessac B, et al. Localisation immunohistochimique du cytochrome P450$_{scc}$ dans les oligodendrocytes de rat en culture. *C R Acad Sci [III]* 1989;308:165–170.

13. Hu ZY, Bourreau E, Jung-Testas I, et al. Neurosteroids: oligodendrocyte mitochondria convert cholesterol to pregnenolone. *Proc Natl Acad Sci USA* 1987;84: 8215–8219.

14. Warner M, Tollet P, Strömstedt M, et al. Endocrine regulation of cytochrome P450 in the rat brain and pituitary gland. *J Endocrinol* 1989;122:341–349.

15. Iwahashi K, Ozaki HS, Tsubaki M, et al. Studies of the immunohistochemical and biochemical localization of the cytochrome P-450$_{scc}$-linked monooxygenase system in the adult rat brain. *Biochim Biophys Acta* 1990;1035:182–189.

16. Haug M, Brain PF. Effects of treatments with testosterone and oestradiol on the attack directed by group gonadectomized male and female mice towards lactating intruders. *Physiol Behav* 1979;23:397–400.

17. Haug M, Spetz JF, Ouss-Schlegel ML, et al. Rôle de la déhydroépiandrostérone et de la prégnènolone dans l'expression du comportement d'agression vis-à-vis de femelles allaitantes chez la souris. *Pathol Biol* 1988;36:995–1001.

18. Haug M, Young J, Robel P, et al. L'inhibition par la déhydroépiandrostérone des réponses agressives de souris femelles castrées vis à vis d'intruses allaitantes est potentialisée par l'androgénisation néonatale. *C R Acad Sci [III]* 1991;312:511–516.

19. Corpéchot C, Leclerc P, Baulieu EE, et al. Neurosteroids: regulatory mechanisms in male rat brain during heterosexual exposure. *Steroids* 1985;45:229–234.

20. Majewska MD, Schwartz RD. Pregnenolone sulfate: an endogenous antagonist of the γ-aminobutyric acid receptor complex in brain. *Brain Res* 1987;404:355–360.

21. Mienville JM, Vicini S. Pregnenolone sulfate antagonizes GABA$_A$ receptor-mediated currents via a reduction of channel opening frequency. *Brain Res* 1989;489:190–194.

22. Majewska MD, Bluet-Pajot MT, Robel P, et al. Pregnenolone sulfate antagonizes barbiturate-induced hypnosis. *Pharmacol Biochem Behav* 1989;33:701–703.

23. Holzbauer M. Physiological aspects of steroids with anaesthetic properties. *Med Biol* 1976;54:227–242.
24. Phillips GH. Structure-activity relationships in steroidal anaesthetics. In: Massley MJ, Millar RA, Sutton JA, eds. *Molecular mechanisms of general anaesthesia.* London: Churchill-Livingstone, 1974;32–47.
25. Selye H. Anaesthetic effects of steroid hormones. *Proc Soc Exp Biol Med* 1941;46:116–121.
26. Majewska MD, Harrison NL, Schwartz RD, et al. Steroid hormone metabolites are barbiturate-like modulators of the GABA receptor. *Science* 1986;232:1004–1007.
27. Roberts E, Bologa L, Flood JF, et al. Effects of dehydroepiandrosterone and its sulfate on brain tissue in culture and on memory in mice. *Brain Res* 1987;40:357–362.
28. Jung-Testas I, Renoir JM, Gasc JM, et al. Estrogen-inducible progesterone receptor in primary cultures of rat glial cells. *Exp Cell Res* 1991;193:12–19.
29. Fraile IG, Pfaff DW, McEwen BS. Progestin receptors with and without estrogen induction in male and female hamster brain. *Neuroendocrinology* 1987;45:487–491.
30. Magdelenat H, Pertuiset BF, Poisson M, et al. Progestin and estrogen receptors in meningioma. Biochemical characterization, clinical and pathological correlations in 42 cases. *Acta Neurochir* 1982;64:199–213.
31. Baulieu EE, Godeau JF, Schorderet M, et al. Steroid induced meiotic division in Xenopus laevis oocytes: surface and calcium. *Nature* 1978;275:593–598.
32. Blondeau JP, Baulieu EE. Progesterone receptor characterized by photoaffinity labelling in the plasma membrane of Xenopus laevis oocytes. *Biochem J* 1984;219:785–792.
33. Finidori-Lepicard J, Schorderet-Slatkine S, Hanoune J, et al. Steroid hormone as regulatory agent of adenylate cyclase. Inhibition by progesterone of the membrane bound enzyme in Xenopus laevis oocytes. *Nature* 1981;292:255–256.
34. Dufy B, Vincent JD, Fleury H, et al. Membrane effects of thyrotropin-releasing hormone and estrogen shown by intracellular recording from pituitary cells. *Science* 1979;104:509–510.
35. Kelly MJ, Moss RL, Dubley CA, et al. The specificity of the response of preoptic-septal area neurons to estrogen: 17α-estradiol versus 17β-estradiol and the response of extrahypothalamic neurons. *Exp Brain Res* 1977;30:43–52.
36. Pietras RJ, Szego CM. Specific binding site for oestrogen at the outer surfaces of isolated endometrial cells. *Nature* 1977;265:69–72.
37. Smith SS, Waterhouse BD, Woodward DJ. Sex steroid effects on extrahypothalamic CNS. I. Estrogen augments neuronal responsiveness to iontophoretically applied glutamate in the cerebellum. *Brain Res* 1987;422:40–51.
38. Smith SS, Waterhouse BD, Woodward DJ. Sex steroid effects on extrahypothalamic CNS. II. Progesterone, alone or in combination with estrogen, modulates cerebellar responses to amino acid neurotransmitters. *Brain Res* 1987;422:52–62.
39. McEwen BS. Non-genomic and genomic effects of steroids on neuronal activity. *Trends Pharmacol Sci* 1991;12:141–147.
40. Carette B, Poulain P. Excitatory effect of dehydroepiandrosterone, its sulfate ester and pregnenolone sulfate, applied by iontophoresis and pressure, on single

neurons in the septo-preoptic area of the guinea pig. *Neurosci Lett* 1984;45: 205–210.

41. Levitan ES, Schofield PR, Burt DR, et al. Structural and functional basis for GABA$_A$ receptor heterogeneity. *Nature* 1988;335:76–79.

42. Olsen RW. Drug interaction at the GABA receptor-ionophore complex. *Annu Rev Pharmacol Toxicol* 1982;22:245–277.

43. Gee KW, Chang WC, Brinton RE, et al. GABA-dependent modulation of the Cl ionophore by steroids in the rat brain. *Eur J Pharmacol* 1987;136:419–423.

44. Lambert JJ, Peters JA, Cottrell GA. Actions of synthetic and endogenous steroids on the GABA$_A$ receptor. *Trends Pharmacol Sci* 1987;8:224–227.

45. Puia G, Santi MR, Vicini S, et al. Neurosteroids act on recombinant human GABA$_A$ receptors. *Neuron* 1990;4:759–765.

46. Majewska MD, Demirgören S, Spivak CE, et al. The neurosteroid dehydro-epiandrosterone sulfate is an allosteric antagonist of the GABA$_A$ receptor. *Brain Res* 1990;526:143–146.

47. Lanthier A, Patwardhan VV. Sex steroids and 5-en-3β-hydroxysteroids in specific regions of the human brain and cranial nerves. *J Steroid Biochem* 1986;25:445–449.

48. Lacroix C, Fiet J, Benais JP, et al. Simultaneous radioimmunoassay of progesterone, androst-4-enedione, pregnenolone, dehydroepiandrosterone and 17-hydroxyprogesterone in specific regions of human brain. *J Steroid Biochem* 1987;28:317–325.

49. Le Goascogne C, Gouézou M, Robel P, et al. The cholesterol side-chain cleavage complex in human brain white matter. *J Neuroendocrinol* 1989;2:153–156.

IV

Neurosteroids

The Actions of Neurosteroids on Inhibitory Amino Acid Receptors

*C. Hill-Venning, Ph.D., J.J. Lambert, Ph.D., J.A. Peters, Ph.D., and *T.G. Hales, Ph.D.*

*Neuroscience Research Group, Department of Pharmacology and Clinical Pharmacology, University of Dundee, Ninewells Hospital and Medical School, Dundee DD1 9SY, Scotland, U.K.; and *Present address: Department of Anesthesiology, University of California Los Angeles School of Medicine, Center for the Health Sciences, Los Angeles, California 90024–1778*

In 1984 Harrison and Simmonds demonstrated that the steroidal anesthetic alphaxalone (5α-pregnan-3α-ol-11,20-dione) enhanced γ-aminobutyric acid (GABA)$_A$ receptor–mediated depolarizations recorded from a rat brain slice preparation (1). This effect occurred at relatively low aqueous concentrations of the steroid and was stereoselective, because the behaviorally inert 3β-ol isomer, betaxalone, was inactive. These observations suggest a specific mechanism of action for this potent central depressant. Furthermore, because alphaxalone structurally is closely related to a number of endogenously occurring pregnane steroids [which had been known for some time to be anesthetic (2–4)], the exciting prospect was raised that the activity of the GABA$_A$ receptor is influenced by endogenous steroids under physiological or pathophysiological conditions (5). Subsequent biochemical (6–10) and electrophysiological (7,8,11,12) studies soon illustrated that some endogenous steroids, particularly the progesterone metabolites 5α- and 5β-pregnan-3α-ol-20-one, and the deoxycorticosterone metabolite 5α-pregnane-3α,21-diol-20-one (THDOC), are among the most potent GABA modulators known.

Voltage-clamp and patch-clamp studies demonstrated that nanomolar (>10 nM) concentrations of these steroids potentiated GABA-evoked currents by prolonging the GABA channel burst duration (11–14). Additionally, at relatively higher concentrations (>300 nM) these steroids directly activated the GABA$_A$ receptor (11,13,15). Although mechanistically similar to the anesthetic barbiturates (11), the results of barbiturate and steroid combination studies suggested the presence of a distinct steroid binding site (6,10,16). However, because the steroids are highly lipid soluble and the active isomers cause membrane perturbation (17,18), the possibility remained that the effects on the GABA$_A$ receptor were secondary. The demonstration that an intracellularly applied steroid is inactive (19) implies, although not conclusively, a specific site on the GABA$_A$ receptor.

To understand better the molecular mechanism of steroid action, we used patch-clamp techniques to compare the actions of pregnane steroids with those of a number of structurally distinct anesthetics on cloned GABA$_A$ "receptors" of known subunit composition, and on the closely related glycine-activated chloride channel of mouse spinal neurons.

Methods

The Chinese hamster ovary (CHO) cell line, which previously had been transfected with the cDNAs coding for the bovine α_1 and β_1 subunits of the GABA$_A$ receptor (20), was incubated for 48 hr with 1 µM dexamethasone to induce functional GABA "receptor" expression. Embryonic mouse spinal neurons were isolated and cultured as described elsewhere (21). Whole-cell currents were recorded with a List electronics L/M EPC-7 converter headstage and amplifier, using standard patch-clamp techniques. For CHO cells, the extracellular recording solution (in mM) was as follows: NaCl 140, KCl 4.7, MgCl$_2$ 1.2, CaCl$_2$ 2.5, glucose 11, HEPES 5, buffered to pH 7.4. The internal pipette solution (in mM) was as follows: either KCl or CsCl 150, MgCl$_2$ 1, EGTA 0.5, CaCl$_2$ 0.28, HEPES 5, buffered to pH 7.4. For mouse spinal neurons, the extracellular recording solution (in mM) was as follows: NaCl 140, KCl 2.8, MgCl$_2$ 2, CaCl$_2$ 1, HEPES 10, buffered to pH 7.2. The internal recording solution (in mM) was as follows: CsCl 140, MgCl$_2$ 2, CaCl$_2$ 0.1, EGTA 1.1, HEPES 10, buffered to pH 7.2. GABA and glycine were applied by pressure ejection from a modified pipette (1.4 x 10^5 Pa, 10 to 20 msec, 100 µM). In some experiments, GABA (50 µM) was applied via the superfusion system (2 to 4 ml/min^{-1}). All other compounds also were applied in this manner. Experiments were performed at room temperature (17° to 23°C). Whole-cell currents were low-pass filtered (Bessel characteristic) at a cut-off frequency of 0.5 kHz. Qualitative data were reported as the arithmetic mean $\pm$ SE.

Results

Action of Flunitrazepam and Intravenous Anesthetics on a Cloned $\alpha_1\beta_1$ GABA$_A$ Subunit Combination

Stably Transfected CHO Cells—General Properties
Only cells growing in isolation were chosen for study, to avoid possible electrical coupling. The bath application of GABA (50 μM) to such cells, voltage-clamped at –55 mV, produced an inward current for 44% (n = 169) of the cells tested. However, for the agonist-sensitive cells, the current evoked varied considerably (50 pA to 3 nA), perhaps suggesting different levels of receptor expression. Cells giving a relatively large response (>500 pA) to bath-applied GABA (50 μM) were chosen for further experimentation. To such cells, GABA (100 μM) was applied locally by pressure ejection and the influence of the putative modulators was determined.

Flunitrazepam and Pentobarbitone
The γ_2 subunit has been determined essential for imparting a "normal" benzodiazepine sensitivity to the GABA$_A$ receptor complex (22–24). In agreement with these studies, flunitrazepam (1 μM) had little or no effect on the GABA-evoked current of the CHO cells (Figure 1). In contrast with the subunit specificity of benzodiazepines, barbiturates can act on "receptors" formed from only α and β subunits (25). Pentobarbitone (100 μM) produced a well-maintained enhancement of the GABA-evoked current (228 $\pm$ 11% of control, n = 3), which was reversed on washout (Figure 1).

Propofol
We previously demonstrated that the intravenous anesthetic agent propofol (2,6-diisopropylphenol), at concentrations of 1 to 10 μM, enhances GABA-evoked currents recorded from bovine chromaffin cells or rodent central neurons (21). Preliminary experiments suggest that, in common with barbiturates (26) and steroids (11,12), this action is a consequence of a prolongation of channel burst duration (21). The specific binding of [³H]propofol to rat cortical membranes has recently been described (27). Furthermore, radioligand binding experiments with the convulsant [³⁵S]-t-butyl-bicyclophosphorothionate ([³⁵S]TBPS) suggest that it may

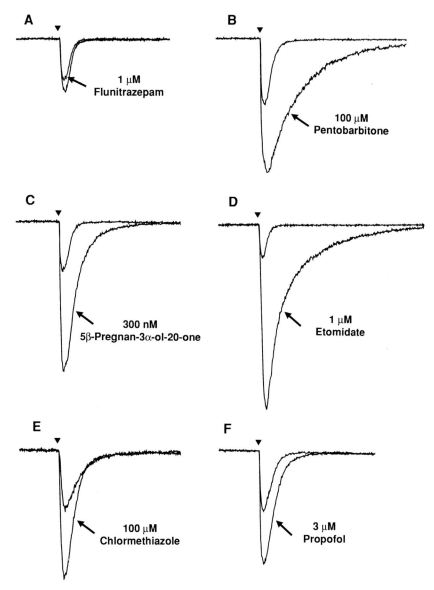

Figure 1. The effect of anesthetics and flunitrazepam on GABA-evoked currents in Chinese hamster ovary cells stably transfected with α_1 and β_1 GABA$_A$ receptor subunits. Each pair of current traces was evoked by locally applied (100 μM) GABA (indicated at ▼) in absence (control) and presence of test drug. Each trace is average of 5 currents. (**A**) In the presence of 1 μM flunitrazepam, the GABA-evoked current was slightly decreased. In contrast, (**B**) pentobarbitone (100 μM), (**C**) 5β-pregnan-3α-ol-20-one (300 nM), (**D**) etomidate (1 μM), (**E**) chlormethiazole (100 μM) and (**F**) propofol (3 μM) all enhanced GABA currents. Scale bar: **A, B, C**, vertical—100 pA, horizontal—1 sec; **D**, vertical—285 pA, horizontal—1.5 sec; **E, F**, vertical—250 pA, horizontal—1.5 sec.

act at a site(s) distinct from either steroids or barbiturates (28). In the present study, propofol (3 μM) produced a well-maintained enhancement of the GABA-evoked current, which was reversed on washout (Figure 1).

Etomidate

The nonbarbiturate intravenous anesthetic etomidate potently displaces [^{35}S]TBPS binding from rat brain membranes (29; T.A. Firth and J.J. Lambert, unpublished observations) and, at relatively high concentrations (30 to 100 μM), induces a bicuculline-sensitive chloride current in mammalian dorsal root ganglion neurons (30). The GABA-induced whole-cell current recorded from the CHO cells was rapidly and reversibly enhanced (Figure 1) by 1 μM etomidate (416 ± 19% of control, n = 5).

Chlormethiazole

We previously demonstrated that the anxiolytic and anticonvulsant chlormethiazole (30 to 100 μM) enhances GABA-evoked currents in bovine chromaffin cells by prolonging GABA channel burst duration (31). Similarly, chlormethiazole (100 μM) produced a well-maintained enhancement of the CHO cell GABA current (Figure 1, 215 ± 18% of control, n = 5), which was readily reversed on washout.

5β-Pregnan-3α-ol-20-one

The endogenous steroid 5β-pregnan-3α-ol-20-one (300 nM) rapidly and reversibly enhanced the CHO cell GABA current (Figure 1, 322 ± 26% of control, n = 5). Additionally, on a small proportion of GABA-responsive cells, the bath application of this concentration of the steroid alone induced an inward current. This steroid-induced current was completely blocked by the coapplication of 10 μM bicuculline and greatly enhanced by 10 μM pentobarbitone (data not shown). These data suggest that the inward current is due to the direct activation of the $\alpha_1\beta_1$ subunit complex by the steroid (11).

Pregnane Steroids and the Strychnine-Sensitive Glycine Receptor

The results illustrated in Figure 1, together with those from previous studies (32) suggest that the pregnane steroid–GABA$_A$ receptor interaction is not subunit specific. Because the glycine receptor chloride channel exhibits a high degree of sequence homology with the GABA$_A$ receptor (33), it was of interest to determine whether steroids are active at glycine receptors.

At a holding potential of −60 mV, the local application of glycine (100 μM) elicited an inward current on all spinal neurons tested. Such currents were completely antagonized by 100 nM strychnine (n = 5). In contrast with their effects on GABA currents, alphaxalone (10 μM) and pentobarbitone (100 μM) had little or no effect on glycine-evoked currents (cf. 34). However, both chlormethiazole (100 μM) and propofol (16.8 μM), at concentrations that substantially potentiated GABA currents (Figure 1), enhanced the glycine-evoked current to 165 ± 10% of control (n = 6) and 182 ± 15% of control (n = 8), respectively.

Discussion

The harnessing of molecular cloning and patch-clamp techniques provides a powerful new approach to aid our understanding of the pharmacology of the GABA receptor, and may provide important information on the putative steroid binding site. In confirmation of previous studies using CHO cells (20), the $\alpha_1\beta_1$ subunit combination was insensitive to the benzodiazepine flunitrazepam. However, the steroid 5β-pregnan-3α-ol-20-one, pentobarbitone, etomidate, chlormethiazole and propofol were all active. Patch-clamp studies revealed that these agents potentiate GABA by prolonging the channel burst duration (11,21,26,31), whereas benzodiazepines mainly increase the probability of channel opening (35). Therefore, GABA modulation by the former mechanism does not seem to exhibit a strict subunit requirement. However, it remains puzzling how such diverse chemical structures produce this common molecular effect.

Although the steroid action is apparently not subunit specific (32), a recent study has demonstrated that the magnitude of the steroid potentiation by GABA may be influenced by the α subunit, with chimeras containing the α_1 subunit most effective (36). Additionally, a number of studies now suggest regional differences in the steroid modulation of the $GABA_A$ receptor (6,37). The possibility that these differences are a consequence of variant $GABA_A$ receptors is intriguing (38).

How can we define the structural elements of the receptor protein required for steroid modulation? One approach is identifying steroid-insensitive receptors, comparing their primary amino acid sequences and using site-directed mutagenesis techniques to evaluate their function (39). In this respect, it is interesting that the glycine-receptor chloride channel—although sharing substantial homology with $GABA_A$ subunits, especially in the proposed channel-forming domains (33)—was insensitive to alphaxalone. The recent identification of a novel ρ_1 subunit from retina (40), and the demonstration that GABA receptors formed from retinal RNA are insensitive to barbiturates (to our knowledge steroids have not been tested), also may be worthy of further attention (41). Alternatively, a comparison of invertebrate GABA subunit sequences may be instructive (42,43).

Acknowledgments

The work reported here was supported by grants from the Scottish Hospitals Endowments Research Trust, and Organon Teknika (Turnhout, Belgium). We additionally thank E.A. Barnard for providing the CHO cells, and thank T.G. Smart for technical advice.

References

1. Harrison NL, Simmonds MA. Modulation of the GABA receptor complex by a steroid anaesthetic. *Brain Res* 1984;323:287–292.
2. Atkinson RM, Davis B, Pratt MA, et al. Action of some steroids on the central nervous system of the mouse. II. Pharmacology. *J Med Chem* 1965;8:426–432.
3. Holzbauer M. Physiological aspects of steroids with anaesthetic properties. *Med Biol* 1976;54:227–242.
4. Selye H. Correlations between chemical structure and the pharmacological actions of the steroids. *Endocrinology* 1942;30:437–453.
5. Majewska MD. Steroids and brain activity. Essential dialogue between body and mind. *Biochem Pharmacol* 1987;36:3781–3788.
6. Gee KW, Bolger MB, Brinton RE, et al. Steroid modulation of the chloride ionophore in rat brain: structure-activity requirements, regional dependence and mechanism of action. *J Pharmacol Exp Ther* 1988;241:346–353.
7. Harrison NL, Majewska MD, Harrington JW, et al. Structure-activity relationships for steroid interaction with the γ-aminobutyric acid_A receptor complex. *J Pharmacol Exp Ther* 1987;241:346–353.
8. Majewska MD, Harrison NL, Schwartz RD, et al. Steroid hormone metabolites are barbiturate-like modulators of the GABA receptor. *Science* 1986;232:1004–1007.
9. Morrow AE, Suzdak PD, Paul SM. Steroid hormone metabolites potentiate GABA receptor-mediated chloride ion flux with nanomolar potency. *Eur J Pharmacol* 1987;142:483–485.
10. Turner DM, Ransom RW, Yang JS-J, et al. Steroid anaesthetics and naturally occurring analogs modulate the γ-aminobutyric acid receptor complex at a site distinct from barbiturates. *J Pharmacol Exp Ther* 1989;248:960–966.
11. Callachan H, Cottrell GA, Hather NY, et al. Modulation of the GABA_A receptor by progesterone metabolites. *Proc R Soc Lond (Biol)* 1987;231:359–369.
12. Lambert JJ, Peters JA, Cottrell GA. Actions of synthetic and endogenous steroids on the GABA_A receptor. *Trends Pharmacol Sci* 1987;8:224–227.

13. Barker JL, Harrison NL, Lange GD, et al. Potentiation of γ-aminobutyric-acid-activated chloride conductance by a steroid anaesthetic in cultured rat spinal neurones. *J Physiol* 1987;386:485–501.

14. Harrison NL, Vicini S, Barker JL. A steroid anaesthetic prolongs inhibitory postsynaptic currents in cultured rat hippocampal neurons. *J Neurosci* 1987;7:604–609.

15. Cottrell GA, Lambert JJ, Peters JA. Modulation of GABA$_A$ receptor activity by alphaxalone. *Br J Pharmacol* 1987;90:491–500.

16. Peters JA, Kirkness EF, Callachan H, et al. Modulation of the GABA$_A$ receptor by depressant barbiturates and pregnane steroids. *Br J Pharmacol* 1988;94:1257–1269.

17. Makriyannis A, Yang D-P, Mavromoustakos T. The molecular features of membrane perturbation by anaesthetic steroids: a study using differential scanning calorimetry, small angle X-ray diffraction and solid state ^{2}H NMR. *Ciba Found Symp* 1990;153:172–189.

18. Richards CD, White AE. Additive and non-additive effects of mixtures of short-acting intravenous anaesthetic agents and their significance for theories of anaesthesia. *Br J Pharmacol* 1981;74:161–170.

19. Lambert JJ, Peters JA, Sturgess NC, et al. Steroid modulation of the GABA$_A$ receptor complex: electrophysiological studies. *Ciba Found Symp* 1990;153:56–82.

20. Moss SJ, Smart TG, Porter NM, et al. Cloned GABA receptors are maintained in a stable cell line: allosteric and channel properties. *Eur J Pharmacol* 1990;189:77–88.

21. Hales TG, Lambert JJ. The actions of propofol on inhibitory amino acid receptors of bovine adrenomedullary chromaffin cells and rodent central neurones. *Br J Pharmacol* 1991;(in press).

22. Lüddens H, Wisden W. Function and pharmacology of multiple GABA$_A$ receptor subunits. *Trends Pharmacol Sci* 1991;12:49–51.

23. Pritchett DB, Sontheimer H, Shivers BD, et al. Importance of a novel GABA$_A$ receptor subunit for benzodiazepine pharmacology. *Nature* 1989;338:582–585.

24. Schofield PR. The GABA$_A$ receptor: molecular biology reveals a complex picture. *Trends Pharmacol Sci* 1989;10:476–478.

25. Blair LAC, Levitan ES, Marshall J, et al. Single subunits of the GABA$_A$ receptor form ion channels with properties of the native receptor. *Science* 1988;242:577–580.

26. MacDonald RL, Rogers CJ, Twyman RE. Barbiturate regulation of kinetic properties of the GABA$_A$ receptor channel of mouse spinal neurones in culture. *J Physiol* 1990;417:483–500.

27. Concas A, Santoro G, Mascia MP, et al. The action of the general anaesthetic propofol on GABA$_A$ receptors. In: Biggio G, Costa E, eds. *GABAergic synaptic transmission: molecular, pharmacological & clinical aspects: advances in biochemical psychopharmacology,* vol 46. New York: Raven Press, 1991;(in press).

28. Concas A, Santoro G, Serra M, et al. Neurochemical action of the general anaesthetic propofol on the chloride ion channel coupled with GABA$_A$ receptors. *Brain Res* 1991;542:225–232.

29. Olsen RW, Fischer JB, Dunwiddie TV. Barbiturate enhancement of γ-aminobutyric acid receptor binding and function as a mechanism of anesthesia. In: Roth H, Miller KW, eds. *Molecular and cellular mechanisms of anesthetics.* New York: Plenum Press, 1986;165–177.

30. Robertson B. Actions of anaesthetics and avermectin on GABA$_A$ chloride channels in mammalian dorsal root ganglion neurones. *Br J Pharmacol* 1989;98:167–176.

31. Hales TG, Lambert JJ. The actions of chlormethiazole on the GABA$_A$ receptor of bovine chromaffin cells in culture. *J Physiol* 1988;398:14P.

32. Puia G, Santi MR, Vicini S, et al. Neurosteroids act on recombinant human GABA$_A$ receptors. *Neuron* 1990;4:759–765.

33. Barnard EA, Darlison MG, Seeburg P. Molecular biology of the GABA$_A$ receptor: the receptor/channel superfamily. *Trends Neurosci* 1987;10:502–509.

34. Wu F-S, Gibbs TT, Farb DH. Inverse modulation of γ-aminobutyric acid- and glycine-induced currents by progesterone. *Mol Pharmacol* 1990;37:597–602.

35. Vicini S, Mienville J-M, Costa E. Actions of benzodiazepine and β-carboline derivatives on γ-aminobutyric acid-activated Cl⁻ channels recorded from membrane patches of neonatal rat cortical neurons in culture. *J Pharmacol Exp Ther* 1987;243:1195–1201.

36. Shingai R, Sutherland ML, Barnard EA. Effects of subunit types of the cloned GABA$_A$ receptor on the response to a neurosteroid. *Eur J Pharmacol* 1991;206: 77–80.

37. Gee KW, Lan NC. The GABA$_A$ receptor complex in rat frontal cortex and spinal cord show differential responses to steroid modulation. *Eur J Pharmacol* 1991;(in press).

38. Morrow AL, Pace JR, Purdy RH, et al. Characterization of steroid interactions with γ-aminobutyric acid receptor-gated chloride ion channels: evidence for multiple steroid recognition sites. *Mol Pharmacol* 1990;37:263–270.

39. Pritchett DB, Seeburg PH. γ-Aminobutyric acid type A receptor point mutation increases the affinity of compounds for the benzodiazepine site. *Proc Natl Acad Sci USA* 1991;88:1421–1425.

40. Cutting GR, Lu L, O'Hara B, et al. Cloning of the γ-aminobutyric acid (GABA) ρ$_1$ cDNA: a GABA receptor subunit highly expressed in the retina. *Proc Natl Acad Sci USA* 1991;88:2673–2677.

41. Polenzani L, Woodward RM, Miledi R. Expression of mammalian γ-aminobutyric acid receptors with distinct pharmacology in *Xenopus* oocytes. *Proc Natl Acad Sci USA* 1991;88:4318–4322.

42. Rauh JJ, Lummis SCR, Sattelle DB. Pharmacological and biochemical properties of insect GABA receptors. *Trends Pharmacol Sci* 1990;11:325–329.

43. Vreugdenhil E, Harvey RJ, van Marle A, et al. Molecular biological characterization of ligand-gated ion channel/receptors in *Lymnaea.* In: Kits KS, Boer HH, eds. *Molluscan neurobiology.* Amsterdam: North Holland Publishing Co., 1991;(in press).

The Effects of Estrogen and Progesterone on GABA and Glutamate Responses at Extrahypothalamic Sites

S.S. Smith, Ph.D.

Department of Anatomy, Institute for Neuroscience, Hahnemann University, Philadelphia, Pennsylvania 19102–1192

An emerging concept in neurobiology is that sex steroids exert effects on widespread areas of the CNS, beyond those associated with reproductive control. In addition to classical actions at nuclear receptor sites with ensuing genomic effects, 17β-estradiol and progesterone (P), or specific metabolites, can alter responses of conventional neurotransmitter receptors throughout the brain. In the cerebellum, physiological circulating levels, as well as local application of P enhance inhibitory responses of Purkinje cells to iontophoretically applied γ-aminobutyric acid (GABA) by an average of 50% to 80% at $GABA_A$-specific receptor subtypes [1,2]. This enhancement occurs through formation of the well-characterized 3α-OH-DHP (3α-hydroxy-5α-pregnan-20-one) metabolite [3–5]. This modulatory effect of the steroid, injected at a 5-μM concentration through an indwelling jugular cannula in urethane-anesthetized female rats, is observed by 5 min after exposure to the steroid and persists for 30 to 50 min poststeroid before recovery to control levels of response. Modulatory effects of this steroid on GABA inhibition are observed in the absence of significant alterations in background discharge level, suggesting a specific effect of the steroid on GABA physiology.

Three findings suggest that the modulatory effect of P is due to local formation of 3α-OH-DHP: (i) Local application of P by pressure ejection exerted maximal effects on GABA sensitivity of Purkinje cells after only 9 min of continual exposure. (ii) In contrast, local application of the metabolite produced a significant effect (mean = 70%) on potentiation of GABA responses of these neurons within seconds after exposure to the steroid. No significant effect was produced with the inactive 3β-hydroxy isomer. (iii) In addition, the modulatory actions of P are blocked by prior administration of 17β-*N,N*-diethylcarbamoyl-4-aza-5α-androstan-3-one (Merck, Sharp and Dohme, Rahway, NJ), which inhibits 5α-reductase activity.

3α-OH-DHP was first demonstrated to increase chloride conductance in cultured hippocampal and spinal cord neurons (3,5), and to increase benzodiazepine binding in widespread areas of the CNS. The present studies establish that physiological, circulating levels of the parent compound exert significant GABA modulation through conversion to the active metabolite within an intact circuit of the CNS. In the presence of estradiol [2 µg subcutaneously (s.c.) for 2 days], P increased GABA-evoked inhibition by 79%, a 30% increase above effects on this parameter observed in ovariectomized rats administered P without estrogen priming. Whether estradiol enhances activity of the 5α-reductase or 3β-hydroxysteroid oxidoreductase, as shown in some brain areas (6), has yet to be proven in this system.

In contrast to P's effects, estradiol (100 ng/kg) administered systemically over a 3-min period enhanced excitatory responses of Purkinje cells to glutamate by an average of 68% at 15 to 30 min poststeroid (7), an effect that persisted for the duration of a 2- to 4-hr recording session. That these effects are distinct from classic genomic actions of estradiol is suggested by findings demonstrating that prior administration of tamoxifen (an antiestrogen) or anisomycin (a protein synthesis inhibitor) did not prevent the observed modulatory actions of estradiol on excitatory amino acid (EAA) physiology. In contrast, both blockers have been shown to block classic effects of estradiol on reproductive parameters such as lordosis (8) and luteinizing hormone release. Local administration of estradiol also significantly potentiated Purkinje cell responses, within an intact circuit, to glutamate by an average of 86% within 6 min after continuous pressure application of estradiol, an effect specific for the active β-isomer. The modulatory action of estradiol on excitatory responsiveness of cerebellar neurons is at least partially because of enhancement of responses to the EAA agonist quisqualate (QUIS), the predominant receptor subtype present on Purkinje cells. Estradiol (25 ng) systemically administered to anesthetized rats consistently produced a mean 100% increase in responses of Purkinje cells to iontophoretically administered QUIS, an effect seen by 5 min poststeroid, which recovered to control levels of response by 15 min poststeroid (9). Indirect actions of *N*-methyl-

D-aspartate (NMDA) on excitatory responses of the Purkinje cells also were enhanced by an average of 30% by estradiol administration.

The modulatory action of estradiol on EAA-stimulated values of phosphatidylinositol (PI) turnover may be because of formation of undetermined metabolites or other indirect mechanisms including actions on monoamine systems. However, one possible intracellular mediator of glutamate potentiation by estradiol is at the level of the PI second messenger system, because estradiol exerts potentiating effects on this system in cerebellar slices. PI turnover was assessed in 160-μ cross-chopped cerebellar slices using [^{3}H]inositol. Tissue was obtained from adult female rats previously estradiol-primed with 2 μg s.c. daily for 2 days. After uptake of [^{3}H]inositol under Ca^{2+}-free conditions, slices were treated with 50 pM estradiol in 0.01% ETOH (or vehicle alone), 500 nM tetrodotoxin and 10 mM LiCl in a 3-mM Ca^{2+}-containing buffer for 5 min prior to 20-min exposure to EAA agonists. After termination of the assay and separation of aqueous and organic layers with chromatographic procedures, inositol-phosphate (IP) and PI levels were determined and expressed as a ratio. Estradiol-stimulated values of PI hydrolysis were then calculated as percent of basal. Acute estradiol treatment of cerebellar slices from rats chronically treated with the steroid resulted in a 50% increase in QUIS-stimulated values of PI hydrolysis above basal levels. Acute estradiol application in this system also elevated basal values by 30% but had no effect on EAA-stimulated levels of PI turnover from slices not from estradiol-primed animals. This finding suggests that the background estradiol level may enable the steroid to alter this second messenger system. These results are consistent with electrophysiology data demonstrating that significant actions of estradiol on EAA responses of Purkinje cells are only observed on proestrus and estrus, not on diestrus, when circulating levels of the steroid are low. Although the electrophysiological findings may not be mediated by IPs or diacylglycerol, products of phospholipase C activation, estradiol-induced increases in these second messengers would impact on intracellular Ca^{2+} levels and protein phosphorylation activity in cerebellar neurons, actions linked to altered cellular function.

In contrast to estradiol, P suppresses excitatory responses of Purkinje cells to glutamate at nonspecific EAA receptor subtypes by 40% to 51% (10). Effects on QUIS excitation depend on the background discharge level of the neuron and the presence of other EAAs such as NMDA, which may act indirectly on neighboring pre- or postsynaptic terminals. The observed suppressant effect of P on EAA responses was not secondary to

GABA potentiation by the 5α-reduced metabolite of the steroid, because prior administration of bicuculline did not prevent EAA modulation. However, the effect of P may be mediated indirectly by other agents such as serotonin. The effect of P also depended on the stage of the estrous cycle, suggesting that the background steroid milieu enables this steroid to modulate amino acid physiology.

Actions of both hormones, elevated on proestrus, prior to the night of behavioral estrus, should enhance both excitatory and inhibitory synapses in the cerebellum, when circuit rather than cellular mechanisms are considered. Steroids delivered through the circulation should influence the cerebellum on a network level, rather than at isolated synaptic loci, as do conventional synaptic neurotransmitters. Therefore, to determine neural network effects of estrous hormones on the cerebellar circuitry, female rats were chronically implanted with ensembles of recording microwires. These wires monitored the activity of arrays of individual neurons simultaneously within the olivo-cerebellar circuitry during locomotor behavior, and results were evaluated across hormone states. Behaviorally, the night of estrus is associated with an enhanced activational state, with observed improvements in parameters such as limb coordination, as assessed by faster and more accurate limb trajectory in response to changes in treadmill speed/acceleration and the presentation of hurdles. Purkinje cells in the paravermal cerebellum act as comparators to adjust limb trajectory precisely in response to changes in terrain. Contrast enhancement of both excitatory and inhibitory synapses at the level of this circuit should heighten the resolution of limb adjustment in response to errors or transitions in terrain, and result in faster and more accurate limb trajectory, as is observed on estrus. Consonant with this idea, responses of Purkinje cells to forepaw stimulation, evoked electrically or by natural behavioral events (i.e., stance phase of locomotion), are increased by 30% on estrus, following endogenous elevations in estradiol and progesterone, compared with corresponding values obtained on other days of the cycle (Figure 1A). In Figure 1A, peri-event histograms are constructed around the times for the late thrust stage of the step cycle, the motor correlate for this particular cerebellar neuron. Discharge frequency assessed on estrus (92 spikes/sec) was increased relative to diestrus (70 spikes/sec). In addition, the timing of this evoked discharge was altered across the hormone cycle, as cells tested on estrus began to fire 50 to 60 msec earlier relative to limb movement, and decreased discharge 100 msec earlier than when tested on diestrus. These effects are representative of 35 neurons, tested from 10 rats: on the average, step cycle–correlated discharge from estrous Purkinje cells was 30.2% greater than diestrous Purkinje cells and preceded limb movement by a mean 48.5 msec earlier than did corresponding discharge recorded on diestrus. Similar results were obtained after intraperitoneal (i.p.) injection of 30 ng estradiol, a dose that results in physiological circulating levels of the steroid by 15 min postinjection. These results support the hypothesis that estrous-enhancement of the speed and accuracy of coordinated limb movements is associated with the following: (i) increased gain of the Purkinje cell to sensorimotor input, and (ii) increases in the speed or "anticipation" of response.

In addition, responses of Purkinje cells to olivary discharge are increased by 30% to 40% on estrus or after systemic injection of 30 ng estradiol compared with uninjected diestrus controls, as revealed by cross-correlation analysis of olivo-cerebellar discharge (Figure 1B), a finding that targets the olivo-cerebellar circuit as a CNS site modulated directly by reproductive hormones.

Actions of the steroids at other points in the circuit involved with cerebellar control of limb coordination are possible mechanisms for known behavioral changes produced by proestrous hormones. One such candidate is the dorsal accessory olivary (DAO) nucleus, which functions as an error or event marker to signal changes in the ongoing motor plan to the Purkinje cell comparator. Responses of the DAO to somatosensory input are selectively gated out during movement and gated in during nonmovement as one mechanism by which this structure functions to identify transitions in terrain. Enhanced contrast of excitatory and inhibitory responses as predicted by known cellular actions of proestrous hormones should result in a greater resolution of this selective gating mechanism. Preliminary evidence suggests that the night of behavioral estrus is associated with enhanced olivary response to forepaw stimulation (by 30%, n = 8 cells, 2 rats) during nonmovement, with conversion to an inhibitory response during movement, compared with diestrous values. These results are consistent with the finding that fewer motor errors are committed on the night of behavioral estrus compared with other days of the cycle.

In contrast with stimulatory actions of both estrous hormones, inhibitory effects of progestin compounds alone may mimic actions of the benzodiazepines in their anxiolytic effect, a supposition demonstrated using animal models of anxiety (11,12). As a corollary to this effect, withdrawal from chronic P treatment should increase anxiety. We tested this hypothesis using an animal model, the conditioned defensive burying paradigm. For this procedure, decreases in the latency and increases in the duration of the burial of an electrified prod are indicative of increased anxiety. For this paradigm, female rats were exposed to 4-day P treatment (500 μg daily i.p. in sesame oil) concurrent with estradiol (2 μg daily), for the first 2 days of the injection schedule. On day 5, withdrawal from chronic P treatment produced increases in anxiety as determined by significant decreases (33%) in latency and increases in duration (55%) of prod burial compared with vehicle-treated controls (n = 6). This anxiogenic effect produced by withdrawal from the steroid could be reversed with subsequent administration of P (500 μg i.p.) on day 5 to an estradiol-primed animal. These results suggest that withdrawal from P during the hormone cycle may increase anxiety, and are consistent with modulatory actions of P metabolites at the $GABA_A$ receptor.

In sum, the estrous hormones P and estradiol, through locally formed metabolites such as 3α-OH-DHP, exert an array of psychoactive, sensorimotor actions. These actions may be the result of interactions with conventional CNS neurotransmitters on multiple CNS circuits, distinct from their classic mode of action. The possibility that locally formed metabolites, only some of which have been elucidated, may exert circuit and receptor-specific actions increases the diversity of effects that these hormones may influence.

Figure 1. Cerebellar Purkinje (Pnj) cells exhibit increased responses to afferent input on the night of behavioral estrus, after endogenous increases in circulating estradiol and progesterone. Unit activity is presented from a cerebellar Purkinje cell and dorsal accessory olive (DAO) neuron recorded simultaneously on the night of estrus [after endogenous increases in circulating E2 (estradiol) and P] and diestrus1 (low E2 levels). Discharge monitored using chronically implanted ensembles of microwires in adult female rats to assess activity from these CNS sites during intermittent treadmill locomotion paradigms. Results compared across the days of the estrous cycle.

A: Behaviorally evoked discharge of a Purkinje cell is increased on estrus compared with diestrus. The indicated Purkinje cell discharges maximally during the late thrust (LT) stage of the step cycle. This behaviorally correlated discharge is increased by 31.4% when monitored on estrus compared with diestrus during comparable gait as assessed by videotaped analysis of limb placement. Results represent 10 cells tested in 3 rats.

B: Purkinje cell responses to input from the DAO are enhanced on estrus. Using cross-correlation analysis histograms, constant, short-latency discharge of a Purkinje cell triggered on an olivary spike reveals a monosynaptic olivo-cerebellar connection between the two neurons. For the indicated Purkinje cell, responses to spontaneous olivary input are increased by 30% when assessed on estrus compared with similar values obtained on diestrus. These results represent 8 olivo-cerebellar pairs recorded from 2 rats.

Results from both studies suggest that increased responses of Purkinje neurons to afferent input are observed after increases in circulating levels of E2. These results are consistent with our previous findings demonstrating long-term increases in glutamate sensitivity after local or systemic administration of physiological levels of estradiol.

A

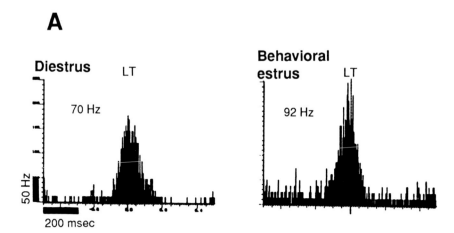

Diestrus

LT

70 Hz

50 Hz

200 msec

Behavioral estrus

LT

92 Hz

Step cycle

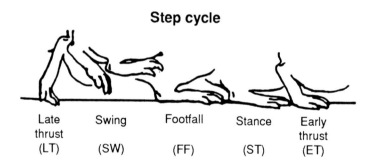

Late thrust	Swing	Footfall	Stance	Early thrust
(LT)	(SW)	(FF)	(ST)	(ET)

B

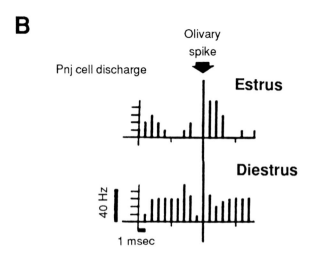

Pnj cell discharge

Olivary spike

Estrus

Diestrus

40 Hz

1 msec

References

1. Smith SS, Waterhouse BD, Chapin JK, et al. Progesterone alters GABA and glutamate responsiveness: a possible mechanism for its anxiolytic action. *Brain Res* 1987;400:353–359.

2. Smith SS, Waterhouse BD, Woodward DJ. Locally applied progesterone metabolites alter neuronal responsiveness in the cerebellum. *Brain Res Bull* 1987;18:739–747.

3. Harrison NL, Majewska MD, Jarrington JW, et al. Structure-activity relationships for steroid interaction with a γ-aminobutyric acid$_A$ receptor complex. *J Pharmacol Exp Ther* 1987;241:346–353.

4. Gee KW, Chang W-C, Brinton RE, et al. GABA-dependent modulation of the Cl⁻ ionophore by steroids in rat brain. *Eur J Pharmacol* 1987;136:419–423.

5. Majewska MD, Harrison NL, Schwartz RD, et al. Steroid hormone metabolites are barbiturate-like modulators of the GABA receptor. *Science* 1986;232:1004–1007.

6. Karavolas HJ, Bertics PJ, Hodges D, et al. Progesterone processing by neuroendocrine structures. In: Celoti F, Naftolin F, Martini L, eds. *Metabolism of hormonal steroids in the neuroendocrine structures.* New York: Raven Press, 1984;149–170.

7. Smith SS, Waterhouse BD, Woodward DJ. Sex steroid effects on extrahypothalamic CNS. I. Estrogen augments neuronal responsiveness to iontophoretically applied glutamate in the cerebellum. *Brain Res* 1987;422:40–51.

8. Parsons B, Rainbow TC, Pfaff DW, et al. Hypothalamic protein synthesis is essential for the activation of the lordosis reflex in the female rat. *Endocrinology* 1982;110:620–624.

9. Smith SS. Estrogen administration increases neuronal responses to excitatory amino acids as a long-term effect. *Brain Res* 1989;503:354–357.

10. Smith SS. Progesterone administration attenuates excitatory amino acid responses of cerebellar Purkinje cells. *Neuroscience* 1991;42:309–320.

11. Bitran D, Hilvers RJ, Kellogg CK. Anxiolytic effects of 3α-hydroxy-5α[β]-pregnan-20-one: endogenous metabolites of progesterone that are active at the GABA$_A$ receptor. *Brain Res* 1991;(in press).

12. Rodriguez-Sierra JF, Howard JL, Pollard GT, et al. Effect of ovarian hormones on conflict behavior. *Psychoneuroendocrinology* 1984;9:293–300.

The 3α-Hydroxy Ring A–Reduced Metabolites of Progesterone and Deoxycorticosterone: Natural Ligands of Central GABA$_A$ Receptors

*Robert H. Purdy, Ph.D., Perry H. Moore Jr., *A. Leslie Morrow, Ph.D., and †Steven M. Paul, M.D.*

*Department of Organic Chemistry, Southwest Foundation for Biomedical Research, San Antonio, Texas 78228; †Section on Molecular Pharmacology, Clinical Neuroscience Branch, National Institute of Mental Health, Bethesda, Maryland 20892; and *Present address: Department of Psychiatry and Center for Alcohol Studies, University of North Carolina School of Medicine, Chapel Hill, North Carolina 27599*

When Selye (1) first reported in 1942 the remarkable anesthetic and sedative properties of several 3α-hydroxy ring A–reduced pregnane and androstane steroids, he recognized a clear separation between hormonal activity and sedative and anesthetic activity. Anesthetic steroids now are known to interact with distinct binding sites of the polypeptide subunits of γ-aminobutyric acid (GABA)$_A$ receptors to potentiate Cl$^-$ conductance allosterically. The relatively high affinity of these 3α-hydroxysteroids for GABA$_A$ receptors (2–8), the presence of unique steroid recognition sites on GABA$_A$ receptor complexes (9,10), and the presence in the brain of both 5α-steroid reductase and 3α-hydroxysteroid oxidoreductase (11–16) have prompted speculation that some of these 3α-hydroxysteroids are endogenous modulators of central GABA$_A$ receptors (2–9). An important objective of our studies has been to demonstrate the presence in the brain of some of these neuroactive steroids, and to investigate the effects of physiological status and acute stress on the levels of these steroids in the brain.

In addition to steroids of gonadal or adrenal origin which can be reduced in the brain to 3α-hydroxysteroids, a variety of neurosteroids such as pregnenolone (3β-hydroxypregn-5-en-20-one) and dehydroepiandrosterone are believed to be formed in the mammalian brain via the classical mevalonate pathway to cholesterol (17). Cultured glial cells of the juvenile rat brain have been shown to oxidize pregnenolone to progesterone (17,18) and reduce progesterone to 3α-hydroxy-5α-pregnan-20-one (allopregnanolone, Figure 1). Similar reactions would convert deoxycorticosterone of adrenal origin to 3α,21-dihydroxy-5α-pregnan-20-one (allotetrahydroDOC, Figure 1) in the brain. Parenthetically, there

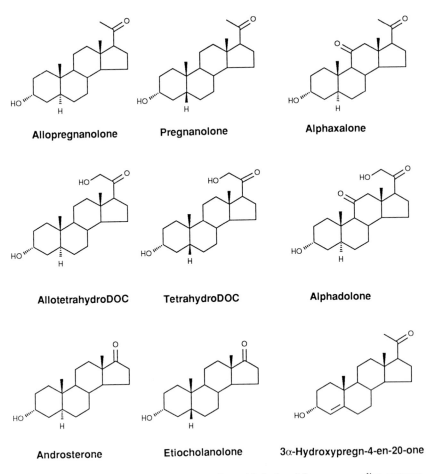

Allopregnanolone	Pregnanolone	Alphaxalone
AllotetrahydroDOC	TetrahydroDOC	Alphadolone
Androsterone	Etiocholanolone	3α-Hydroxypregn-4-en-20-one

Figure 1. Neuroactive steroids. Structures of steroids isolated from mammalian sources, which potentiate GABA-receptor–mediated chloride ion uptake into cerebral synaptoneurosomes.

is no evidence for the 21-hydroxylation of free steroids of this type with a saturated A ring. Therefore, it was not surprising that we found no detectable in vivo conversion of allopregnanolone to allotetrahydroDOC in the rat (19). In addition, androstenedione of gonadal or adrenal origin could be similarly converted to 3α-hydroxy-5α-androstan-17-one (androsterone, Figure 1). We found that androsterone is less active than allopregnanolone or allotetrahydroDOC in potentiation of GABA$_A$ receptor–mediated Cl$^-$ uptake by cerebral cortical synaptoneurosomes (9,19). Because of this finding, we initially developed sensitive and specific radioimmunoassays (RIAs) for detecting >25-pg amounts of allopregnanolone and allotetrahydroDOC (20,21) and prepared them as the 9α,11α,12α-[^{3}H]labeled derivatives (19). Later, a sensitive and specific RIA was obtained for detecting >25-pg amounts of 3α-hydroxy-5β-pregnan-20-one (pregnanolone, Figure 1). In all cases, steroids were purified from tissue extracts by high-performance liquid chromatography (HPLC) before RIA.

Analyses of the levels in the rat brain of the other potential neuroactive steroids shown in Figure 1 are performed by mass spectroscopy. These metabolites include alphaxalone and alphadolone formed by ring A–reduction and 11β-hydroxyl group oxidation of 11β-hydroxyprogesterone and corticosterone, respectively; androsterone and etiocholanolone formed by ring A–reduction of androst-4-ene-3,17-dione; and 3α-hydroxy-pregn-4-en-20-one formed by 3-keto group reduction of progesterone.

Allopregnanolone in the Female Rat Brain

Allopregnanolone was measured in ovarian venous blood by Ichikawa and co-workers (22) and Holzbauer (23) using thin-layer or paper chromatography followed by gas-liquid chromatography. The researchers independently found that the level of allopregnanolone paralleled the rise and fall of plasma progesterone, reaching a maximal level of 450 ng/ml in ovarian venous plasma. Holzbauer and co-workers (24) also found that the amount of allopregnanolone secreted in adrenal venous blood was comparable to that produced by the ovary. However, the methodology used in their studies is not sensitive enough to measure allopregnanolone in purified venous blood or brain tissue.

Analyses were first performed on tissue from various regions of the female rat brain from 5 animals either in proestrus or estrus. No significant differences were found between the different brain regions. The level of allopregnanolone averaged 4.1 ± 1.0 ng/g (mean ± SE) in the cerebral cortex of the animals in proestrus, and 5.0 ± 1.3 ng/g in the cortex of the animals in estrus. These values are similar to those of circulating progesterone in ng/ml. In further work, the cerebral cortex was used for analysis of allopregnanolone. Only a low level of pregnanolone (about 10%) was found in the rat brain and plasma compared with the level of allopregnanolone. In adrenalectomized (ADX)-ovariectomized animals, 1.1 ± 0.1 ng allopregnanolone/g cortex were detected. Similarly, the cerebral cortex had 2.1 ± 0.5 ng/g allopregnanolone in juvenile females, 2.3 ± 0.2 ng/g in diestrus animals, and 3.0 ± 1.6 ng/g in aged females. In the latter four circumstances, no circulating progesterone was detectable. These low levels of allopregnanolone in the cortex are attributed to de novo synthesis in the brain of allopregnanolone from pregnenolone. In contrast, at day 15 of gestation, allopregnanolone levels reached 12.3 ± 1.0 ng/g in the cortex, where 2.8 ± 0.2 ng/g of pregnanolone also were found. This level of allopregnanolone, about 40 nM, gave a 30% to 40% potentiation of muscimol-stimulated [^{36}Cl$^-$] uptake in synaptoneurosomes from the cerebral cortex (4). Indeed, this level of potentiation of GABA$_A$ receptor function is comparable to that produced by the potent benzodiazepine diazepam (1 μM) and clonazepam (1 μM) in an identical assay of muscimol-stimulated [^{36}Cl$^-$] uptake (25). Therefore, allopregnanolone is postulated to have physiological significance in augmenting GABA-mediated inhibition in the CNS in pregnancy.

Allopregnanolone and AllotetrahydroDOC in the Stressed Male Rat Brain

Allopregnanolone, but not allotetrahydroDOC, was detectable (21) in both the cerebral cortex (2.4 ± 0.3 ng/g) and hypothalamus (1.7 ± 1.0 ng/g) of control (nonstressed) adult male Sprague-Dawley rats (n = 24). Similarly, allopregnanolone was still measurable (≥ 3 ng/g or 100 times the minimal detectable level of 25 pg/g) in the cerebral cortex of ADX rats (21). This finding supports the hypothesis that allopregnanolone biosynthesis occurs in the brain from progesterone formed in situ from pregnenolone.

Normal and ADX male rats were subjected to acute stress by swimming for 5 or 10 min in water (22°C). After swimming, the rats were removed from the water, gently dried with towels and placed in plastic cages containing bedding, until sacrifice (0 to 2 hr after swim stress). Swim stress caused rapid (<5 min) and robust (four- to 20-fold) increases of allopregnanolone and allotetrahydroDOC in the cerebral cortex, hypothalamus and plasma of intact animals. These neuroactive steroids progressively declined in the brain until control levels were reached 2 hr after swim stress. Neither steroid was detectable in the plasma of ADX rats before or after swim stress. However, allopregnanolone was found in the cortex of ADX rats (2.8 ± 0.7 ng/g) immediately after 10 min of swim stress. Adrenalectomy prevented any detectable level of allotetrahydroDOC in the cortex or plasma.

We believe that the stress-induced increases in brain levels of allopregnanolone and allotetrahydroDOC may have important behavioral and neuroendocrine consequences. These steroids both produce anticonflict and anxiolytic effects in rodents. Such behavioral effects probably represent adaptive responses of the animals to stress. In addition, GABA also has been shown to inhibit the release of corticotropin-releasing factor (CRF) from the hypothalamus in vitro (26). Thus, stress-induced increases in allopregnanolone could result in a diminished release of CRF and, consequently, decreased adrenocorticotropic hormone/corticosterone. The consequence would be a novel feedback loop for decreasing the heightened activity of the hypothalamic-pituitary-adrenal axis after stress.

Acknowledgments

We are grateful for the collaboration of Drs. Nobuyoshi Hagino, Tasumi Yamaguchi and V. Daniel Castracane, on studies of the female rat brain.

References

1. Selye H. Correlations between the chemical structure and the pharmacological actions of the steroids. *Endocrinology* 1942;30:437–453.
2. Majewska MD, Harrison NL, Rochelle D, et al. Steroid hormone metabolites are barbiturate-like modulators of the GABA receptor. *Science* 1986;232:1004–1007.
3. Harrison NL, Majewska MD, Harrington JW, et al. Structure-activity relationships for steroid interaction with the γ-aminobutyric acid$_A$ receptor complex. *J Pharmacol Exp Ther* 1987;241:346–353.
4. Morrow AL, Suzdak PD, Paul SM. Steroid hormone metabolites potentiate GABA receptor-mediated chloride ion flux with nanomolar potency. *Eur J Pharmacol* 1987;142:483–485.
5. Gee KW, Bolger MB, Brinton RE, et al. Steroid modulation of the chloride ionophore in rat brain: structure-activity requirements, regional dependence and mechanism of action. *J Pharmacol Exp Ther* 1988;246:803–812.
6. Gee KW, Chang W-C, Brinton RE, et al. GABA-dependent modulation of the Cl⁻ ionophore by steroids in rat brain. *Eur J Pharmacol* 1987;136:419–423.

7. Peters JA, Kirkness EF, Callachan H, et al. Modulation of the GABA$_A$ receptor by depressant barbiturates and pregnane steroids. *Br J Pharmacol* 1988;94:1257–1269.

8. Turner DM, Ransom RW, Yang JS-J, et al. Steroid anesthetics and naturally occurring analogs modulate the γ-aminobutyric acid receptor complex at a site distinct from barbiturates. *J Pharmacol Exp Ther* 1989;248:960–966.

9. Morrow AL, Pace JR, Purdy RH, et al. Characterization of steroid interactions with γ-aminobutyric acid receptor-gated chloride ion channels: evidence for multiple steroid recognition sites. *Mol Pharmacol* 1990;37:263–270.

10. Lan NC, Chen J-S, Belelli D, et al. A steroid recognition site is functionally coupled to an expressed GABA$_A$-benzodiazepine receptor. *Eur J Pharmacol (Mol Pharmacol Sect)* 1990;188:403–406.

11. Rommerts FFG, van der Molen HJ. Occurrence and localization of 5α-steroid reductase, 3α- and 17β-hydroxysteroid dehydrogenases in hypothalamus and other brain tissues of the male rat. *Biochim Biophys Acta* 1971;248:489–502.

12. Robinson JA, Karavolas HJ. Conversion of progesterone by rat anterior pituitary tissue to 5α-pregnane-3,20-dione and 3α-hydroxy-5α-pregnan-20-one. *Endocrinology* 1973;93:430–435.

13. Jung-Testas I, Hu ZY, Baulieu EE, et al. Neurosteroids: biosynthesis of pregnenolone and progesterone in primary cultures of rat glial cells. *Endocrinology* 1989;125:2083–2091.

14. Krieger NR, Scott RG. 3α-Hydroxysteroid oxidoreductase in rat brain. *J Neurochem* 1984;42:1866–1870.

15. Melcangi RC, Celotti F, Ballabio M, et al. 5α-Reductase activity in isolated and cultured neuronal and glial cells of the rat. *Brain Res* 1990;516:229–236.

16. Barnea A, Hajibeigi A, Trant JM, et al. Expression of steroid metabolizing enzymes by aggregating fetal brain cells in culture: a model for developmental regulation of the progesterone 5α-reductase pathway. *Endocrinology* 1990;127:500–502.

17. Baulieu E-E, Robel P. Neurosteroids: a new brain function? *J Steroid Biochem Mol Biol* 1990;37:395–403.

18. Jung-Testas I, Hu ZY, Baulieu EE, et al. Neurosteroids: biosynthesis of pregnenolone and progesterone in primary cultures of rat glial cells. *Endocrinology* 1989;125:2083–2091.

19. Purdy RH, Morrow AL, Blinn JR, et al. Synthesis, metabolism, and pharmacological activity of 3α-hydroxysteroids which potentiate GABA-receptor-mediated chloride ion uptake in rat cerebral cortical synaptoneurosomes. *J Med Chem* 1990;33:1572–1581.

20. Purdy RH, Moore PH, Jr., Rao PN, et al. Radioimmunoassay of 3α-hydroxy-5α-pregnan-20-one in rat and human plasma. *Steroids* 1990;55:290–296.

21. Purdy RH, Morrow AL, Moore PH, Jr., et al. Stress-induced elevations of γ-aminobutyric acid type A receptor-active steroids in the rat brain. *Proc Natl Acad Sci USA* 1991;88:4553–4557.

22. Ichikawa S, Sawada T, Nakamura Y, et al. Ovarian secretion of pregnane compounds during the estrous cycle and pregnancy in rats. *Endocrinology* 1974;94:1615–1620.

23. Holzbauer M. Physiological variations in the ovarian production of 5α-pregnane derivatives with sedative properties in the rat. *J Steroid Biochem* 1975;6:1307–1310.

24. Holzbauer M, Birmingham MK, De Nicola AF, et al. *In vivo* secretion of 3α-hydroxy-5α-pregnan-20-one, a potent anaesthetic steroid, by the adrenal gland of the rat. *J Steroid Biochem* 1985;22:97–102.

25. Morrow AL, Paul SM. Benzodiazepine enhancement of γ-aminobutyric acid-mediated chloride ion flux in rat brain synaptoneurosomes. *J Neurochem* 1988;50:302–306.

26. Calogero AE, Gallucci WT, Chrousos GP, et al. Interaction between GABAergic neurotransmission and rat hypothalamic corticotropin-releasing hormone secretion *in vitro*. *Brain Res* 1988;463:28–36.

A Steroid Recognition Site Associated with Central GABA$_A$ Receptors

*Nancy C. Lan, Ph.D., Michael B. Bolger, Ph.D., *Robert Purdy, Ph.D., and Kelvin W. Gee, Ph.D.*

*Department of Molecular Pharmacology and Toxicology, and Department of Pharmaceutical Sciences, University of Southern California School of Pharmacy, Los Angeles, California 90033; and *Department of Organic Chemistry, Southwest Foundation for Biomedical Research, San Antonio, Texas 78228*

Although the ability of pregnane steroids to affect brain excitability and, consequently, animal behavior, has long been documented (1), the site and mechanism of action of these steroids have been elucidated only recently (for review see refs. 2 and 3). Compelling evidence suggests the existence of a unique steroid recognition site on the γ-aminobutyric acid(GABA)$_A$ receptor, which can interact with pregnane steroids with high affinity and structural specificity (2,3). These steroids have been shown to interact allosterically with other GABA$_A$ receptor modulators such as benzodiazepines (BZDs) and barbiturates to potentiate GABA-induced changes in chloride channel conductance. This GABAergic mechanism of action of pregnane steroids coincides with the observed CNS-mediated pharmacological actions of these steroids, which include sedative-hypnotic, anticonvulsant and anxiolytic effects.

Evidence for the Existence of a Steroid Recognition Site Associated with the GABA$_A$ Receptor

Early electrophysiological (4) and ligand-binding studies (5) of the synthetic pregnane steroid alphaxalone (5α-pregnan-3α-ol-11,20-dione), indicating that it could potentiate GABA-mediated inhibition, provided the initial hint that pregnane steroids might interact with the GABA$_A$

103

receptor. Following these initial observations, electrophysiological experiments showed that, like alphaxalone, both 5α- and 5β-reduced, 3α-hydroxylated metabolites of progesterone and deoxycorticosterone are capable of enhancing GABA-evoked chloride channel conductance (6,7). Additionally, these steroids are capable of modulating, in a barbiturate-like manner, [^{3}H]flunitrazepam ([^{3}H]FLU), [^{3}H]muscimol and [^{35}S]-t-butyl-bicyclophosphorothionate ([^{35}S]TBPS) binding to the BZD site, the GABA_A receptor and a site closely associated with the chloride channel of the receptor complex, respectively (8). Thus, barbiturates and steroids were first proposed to share a common site of action on the GABA_A receptor (8).

However, several lines of evidence provided by subsequent electrophysiological and biochemical studies disputed the hypothesis of a common site of action. Electrophysiologically, barbiturates potentiated steroid-induced currents (7,9). In binding studies, sodium pentobarbital enhanced 3α-hydroxy-5α-pregnan-20-one (3α-OH-DHP) potentiation of [^{3}H]FLU binding and the dissociation of [^{35}S]TBPS binding initiated by a saturating concentration of 3α-OH-DHP (10). These observations were inconsistent with the idea of a common site of action. The observations that steroids could potentiate [^{3}H]FLU binding, and that the BZD antagonist Ro15 1788 did not block the steroids' effect on GABA responses (7,11,12), further support the hypothesis that these steroids interact with the GABA_A receptor through a novel site, distinct from either the barbiturate or BZD sites. Recent studies using recombinant cDNA clones of GABA_A receptors demonstrate the ability of steroids to modulate [^{3}H]FLU binding and potentiate GABA-evoked current in cells that expressed the receptor subunits transiently. Thus, evidence suggests that the steroid recognition site is in fact an integral part of the GABA_A receptor protein complex (13,14).

Structure-Activity Requirements of a Novel Steroid Recognition Site

The structure-activity requirements for specific interaction with the steroid recognition site on the GABA_A receptor have been studied in the binding assays (9,15,16) and electrophysiological studies (5,9,16) described in the text above. The major conclusion from these studies is that the 3α-hydroxy configuration is essential because the 3β-hydroxy analogues were devoid of activity and because hormonal steroids such as progesterone and deoxycorticosterone were inactive. However, the number of analogues evaluated in these studies was limited.

Table 1. Allosteric inhibition of 2 nM [^{35}S]TBPS binding to rat cortical P$_2$ homogenates by various steroids

Steroids	IC$_{50}$ (nM)
A. 5α-pregnan-3α-ol-20-one	30 ± 4
B. 5β-pregnan-3α-ol-20-one	58 ± 13
C. 5α-pregnan-3α,21-diol-20-one	77 ± 7
D. 5β-pregnan-3α,21-diol-20-one	145 ± 13
E. 21-chloro-5α-pregnan-3-ol-20-one	80
F. 5α-pregnan-3α,21-diol-20-one 21-acetate	90
G. 5α-pregnan-3β-ol-20-one	>10^5
H. 5α-pregnan-3,20-dione	>10^6
I. 5α-pregnan-3α-ol-11,20-dione	264 ± 49
J. 5α-pregnan-3α,11β-diol-20-one	>10^6
K. 5α-pregnan-3α,11α-diol-20-one	>10^6

IC$_{50}$ is the concentration of steroid that produces half-maximal inhibition of [^{35}S]TBPS binding. All assays performed in the presence of 5 μM GABA using rat cortical P$_2$ homogenates.

We used allosteric inhibition of [^{35}S]TBPS binding to rat brain cortical P$_2$ homogenate as an assay to assess the rank order potency of more than 60 steroids in order to probe the structure-activity relationship in detail. Table 1 shows IC$_{50}$s (concentration of steroid that produces half-maximal inhibition of 2 nM [^{35}S]TBPS binding) of several steroids to illustrate important structural features observed. Among the steroids examined so far, the endogenous progesterone and deoxycorticosterone metabolites, 3α-OH-DHP and 5α-tetrahydrodeoxycorticosterone (5α-THDOC) are the most potent. The 5β-reduced pregnanes have less activity compared with their epimers (in Table 1, compare A and B, C and D). The hydroxyl group at the C-21 position appears nonessential for activity because both 21-chloro (E) and 21-acetate (F) derivatives have similar activity as the parent compound. In contrast, the 3α-hydroxyl group appears essential for activity because neither the 3β-hydroxyl isomer (G) nor the ketone (H) derivative was active. Introduction of a ketone group at the C-11 position reduces the potency (compare A and I); and the reduction of the C-11 ketone to an α- or β-hydroxyl (J and K) further reduces the potency. This rank order potency is consistent with that observed in studies using the potentiation of muscimol-stimulated $^{36}Cl^-$ uptake in synaptoneurosomes as a specific response (17). The presence of sedative-hypnotic, anticonvulsant and anxiolytic effects of these steroids is, in general, consistent with their observed in vitro potencies in the assays described in the text above. Thus, compounds A–F and I were found to have these pharmacological properties; whereas H and G were found inactive (18,19). Steroids J and K were weak sedatives compared with A and I (20).

Heterogeneity of Steroid Recognition Sites

Recent cloning of the $GABA_A$ receptor subunits (for review see refs. 21 and 22) supports the long-standing pharmacological and biochemical evidence for the existence of a heterogeneous population of BZD sites associated with the $GABA_A$ receptor. In light of these findings, we recently investigated whether heterogeneity of steroid sites also exists. Through the use of the [^{35}S]TBPS binding and $^{36}Cl^-$ uptake studies, we found that the absolute potencies for 3α-OH-DHP and THDOC were at least four times greater in the frontal cortex than in the spinal cord (i.e., lower IC_{50} in the cortex). Remarkably, the 5β epimer of THDOC, which had an IC_{50} of 145 nM against [^{35}S]TBPS binding in the frontal cortex, was incapable of modulating [^{35}S]TBPS binding in the spinal cord under the same experimental conditions (23). Moreover, the structure-activity requirements were different between the frontal cortex and the spinal cord. This study demonstrates that neurosteroids can differentially modulate [^{35}S]TBPS in a regionally dependent manner, and shows that subtypes of steroid sites may exist. Consistent with this view, we recently found that expressed $GABA_A$ receptors composed of different recombinant receptor subunits respond differently to 3α-OH-DHP. Correspondingly, maximal steroid potentiation of [^{3}H]FLU binding to the $α_3β_1γ_2$ receptor complex was at least twice as great as that observed with the $α_2β_1γ_2$ and $α_1β_1γ_2$ combinations. Further studies will be required to support the hypothesis that the observed differential sensitivity of recombinant receptors to neurosteroids is responsible for regionally specific responses demonstrated in different brain regions. Recent evidence for the existence of heterogeneous populations of various $GABA_A$ receptor subunits in different brain regions (22), however, favors this notion. Furthermore, it would be reasonable to predict that different subtypes of the receptor may exist that have different structure-activity requirements for neurosteroids.

Conclusion

Based on the pharmacological, biochemical and recombinantly expressed receptor studies, the existence of a steroid recognition site associated with the central $GABA_A$ receptor has become a cogent argument. The ability of endogenously occurring neurosteroids to modulate the $GABA_A$ receptor potently favors the idea that perhaps these steroids play a physiological role in the regulation of brain excitability. Furthermore, the probability is high of developing endogenous or synthetic neurosteroids into therapeutically useful sedative-hypnotic, anticonvulsant and anxiolytic drugs, based on our understanding of the mechanism(s) of action of these steroids. The ability to use expressed recombinant receptors with differential sensitivity to neurosteroids for screening steroids also may prove a useful tool in the development of a novel class of steroid-based therapeutic agents.

References

1. Selye H. The antagonism between anesthetic steroid hormones and penta-methyllenetetrazole (metrazol). *J Lab Clin Med* 1942;27:1051–1053.
2. Gee KW. Steroid modulation of the GABA/benzodiazepine receptor-linked chloride ionophore. *Mol Neurobiol* 1988;2:291–317.
3. Lan NC, Bolger MB, Gee KW. Identification and characterization of a pregnane steroid recognition site that is functionally coupled to an expressed $GABA_A$ receptor. *Neurochem Res* 1991;16:347–356.
4. Schofield CN. Potentiation of inhibition by general anesthetics in neurones of the olfactory cortex in vitro. *Pflügers Arch* 1980;38:249–255.
5. Harrison NL, Majewska MD, Harrington JW, et al. Structure-activity relationships for steroid interaction with the gamma-aminobutyric acid-A receptor complex. *J Pharmacol Exp Ther* 1987;24:346–353.
6. Cottrell GA, Lambert JJ, Mistry D. Alphaxalone potentiates GABA and activates the $GABA_A$ receptor of mouse spinal neurones in culture. *J Physiol* 1987; 382:132.
7. Cottrell GA, Lambert JJ, Peters JA. Modulation of $GABA_A$ receptor activity by alphaxalone. *Br J Pharmacol* 1987;90:491–500.
8. Majewska MD, Harrison NL, Schwartz RD, et al. Steroid metabolites are barbiturate-like modulators of the GABA receptor. *Science* 1986;232:1004–1007.
9. Peters JA, Kirkness EF, Callachan H, et al. Modulation of the $GABA_A$ receptor by depressant barbiturates and pregnane steroids. *Br J Pharmacol* 1988;94:1257–1269.
10. Gee KW, Bolger MB, Brinton RE, et al. Steroid modulation of the chloride ionophore in rat brain: structure activity requirements, regional dependence and mechanism of action. *J Pharmacol Exp Ther* 1988;246:803–812.

11. Barker HL, Harrison NL, Lange GD, et al. Voltage clamp studies of the potentiation of GABA-activated chloride conductance by alphaxalone and a reduced metabolite of progesterone. *J Physiol* 1986;355:838.

12. Harrison NL, Simmonds MA. Modulation of the GABA receptor complex by a steroid anesthetic. *Brain Res* 1984;323:287–292.

13. Lan NC, Chen JS, Belelli D, et al. A steroid recognition site is functionally coupled to an expressed GABA$_A$-benzodiazepine receptor. *Eur J Pharmacol (Mol Pharmacol Sect)* 1990;188:403–406.

14. Puia G, Santi M, Vicini S, et al. Neurosteroids act on recombinant human GABA$_A$ receptors. *Neuron* 1990;4:759–765.

15. Gee KW, Brinton RE, Chang WC, et al. Gamma-aminobutyric acid-dependent modulation of the chloride ionophore by steroids in rat brain. *Eur J Pharmacol* 1987;136:419–423.

16. Turner DM, Ransom RW, Yang JS, et al. Steroid anesthetics and naturally occurring analogs modulate the gamma-aminobutyric acid receptor complex at a site distinct from barbiturates. *J Pharmacol Exp Ther* 1989;248:960–966.

17. Purdy RH, Morrow AL, Blinn JR, et al. Synthesis, metabolism, and pharmacological activity of 3α-hydroxy steroids which potentiate GABA-receptor mediated chloride ion uptake in rat cerebral cortical synaptoneurosomes. *J Med Chem* 1990;33:1572–1581.

18. Belelli D, Gee KW. Anticonvulsant profile of the progesterone metabolite 5α-pregnan-3α-ol-20-one. *Eur J Pharmacol* 1989;166:325–329.

19. Hogskilde S, Wagner J, Carl P, et al. Anticonvulsive properties of pregnanolone emulsion compared with althesin and thiopentone in mice. *Br J Anaesth* 1988;61:462–467.

20. Philips GH. Structure-activity relationships in steroidal anaesthetics. *J Steroid Biochem* 1975;6:607–613.

21. Olsen RW, Tobin AJ. Molecular biology of GABA$_A$ receptors. *FASEB J* 1990;4:1469–1480.

22. Vicini S. Pharmacologic significance of the structural heterogeneity of the GABA$_A$ receptor-chloride ion channel complex. *Neuropsychopharmacology* 1991;4:9–15.

23. Gee KW, Lan NC. The GABA$_A$ receptor complex in rat frontal cortex and spinal cord show differential responses to steroid modulation. *Mol Pharmacol* 1991;(in press).

Neurosteroids: GABA-Agonistic and GABA-Antagonistic Modulators of the GABA$_A$ Receptor

Maria Dorota Majewska, Ph.D.

Laboratory of Neuropharmacology, Addiction Research Center, National Institute on Drug Abuse, Baltimore, Maryland 21224

Two types of receptors, the ionotropic GABA$_A$ receptor and the metabolotropic (G protein–coupled) GABA$_B$ receptor are activated by γ-aminobutyric acid (GABA), a principal inhibitory neurotransmitter in the CNS. The ubiquitous GABA$_A$ receptor is a protein tetra- or pentamer (1), the activation of which by agonists opens the associated chloride channel, leading to increased chloride transport, which usually results in hyperpolarization of the neuronal membrane. GABA$_A$ receptors in the CNS exist in different combinations of polypeptide subunits (α, β, γ, δ, z) forming the receptors with distinct sensitivities to GABA and different ion gating capacities (for review see refs. 2 and 3).

Activity of the GABA$_A$ receptor can be modified by several psychotropic drugs such as benzodiazepines, barbiturates, or convulsants, which act at different domains of the receptor. Recently it became evident that several synthetic and endogenous steroids also directly regulate function of GABA$_A$ receptors in a bimodal fashion. This finding stemmed from two independent experimental approaches. One group of investigators discovered this phenomenon while studying the electrophysiological effects of the steroidal anesthetic alphaxalone (4). I deduced and described the existence of this interaction (5) based on my observation that cholesterol—used originally as a modifier of membrane fluidity—altered GABA binding to the GABA$_A$ receptor.

GABA$_A$ receptors can be regulated by steroids of peripheral origin which, because of their lipophilicity, easily penetrate the blood-brain barrier, and by the "neurosteroids," synthesized locally in the brain (6; see also Baulieu and Robel et al., *this volume*). Neurosteroids, produced mainly in the glial compartment, are not merely structural components of CNS tissues but rather are the brain parahormones, the CNS levels of which change dynamically in various physiological and pathological situations (6). The term *neurosteroids* encompasses pregnenolone (P), dehydroepiandrosterone (DHEA) and their sulfate (S) and lipid (L) esters, as well as their metabolites, including progesterone and the products of its enzymatic reduction, such as dihydroprogesterone and tetrahydroprogesterone (5α-pregnane-3α-ol-20-one, THP).

Because GABA plays a key role in controlling neuronal excitability, the bimodal pattern of regulation of GABA$_A$ receptors by neurosteroids may underlie the spectrum of neurobiological and psychological events accompanied by changing levels of endogenous steroids. This chapter describes the agonistic and antagonistic regulation of GABA$_A$ receptors by neurosteroids, documented by biochemical, electrophysiological and behavioral observations.

GABA-Agonistic Neurosteroids: Biochemical and Electrophysiological Evidence

The endogenous and synthetic steroids—which contain reduced A ring at C-5 in the α or β position, hydroxyl at the 3α-position and an electronegative atom (usually oxygen) at C-17 or C-20—behave as allosteric agonists of the GABA$_A$ receptor (4,7,8). The most potent (active at nanomolar concentrations) naturally occurring steroids with allosteric GABA-agonistic features are THP, tetrahydrodeoxycorticosterone (5α-pregnane-3α,21-diol-20-one, THDOC) (7–9), and androsterone (5α-androstan-3α-ol-17-one) (10,11).

The modulatory actions of GABA-agonistic steroids resemble the effects of anesthetic barbiturates, manifested by the following actions: i) enhancement of GABA (or its agonist) and benzodiazepine binding to brain membranes (7,8,12); ii) inhibition of binding of the radiolabeled convulsant t-butyl-bicyclophosphorothionate (TBPS) to the GABA$_A$ receptor–operated chloride channel in a noncompetitive manner (7); iii) enhancement of GABA-induced chloride transport in synaptoneurosomes (7,11); and iv) potentiation of the GABA$_A$ receptor–mediated current in neurons (7,8,10). GABA-enhancing effects can be observed at nanomolar concentrations of active steroids (threshold concentrations for enhancement are 10 to 30 nM), but at slightly higher concentrations these steroids also directly open the $GABA_A$ receptor–operated chloride channel in neurons (7,8,13). The $GABA_A$ receptor active steroids prolong the electrophysiological responses to GABA because of increased burst duration of the channel currents elicited by GABA (8,14).

Although *prima facie*, the biochemical and electrophysiological actions of GABA-agonistic steroids appeared similar to those of barbiturates, more meticulous tests revealed that the sites of action of these two groups of modulators may not be the same. Specifically, the potentiating effects of barbiturates and steroids on the binding of [³H]muscimol and [³H]flunitrazepam in synaptosomes, and on stimulation of [³⁶Cl⁻] transport in synaptoneurosomes and Cl⁻ currents in neurons, were shown to be additive or synergistic (10,11).

GABA-Antagonistic Neurosteroids: Biochemical and Electrophysiological Evidence

In contrast to THP, THDOC, or androsterone, which act as allosteric agonists of the $GABA_A$ receptor, neurosteroids such as PS and DHEAS behave primarily as noncompetitive antagonists of this receptor (15–20).

I have shown that PS bimodally alters binding of the GABA agonist, [³H]muscimol, to the $GABA_A$ receptor in synaptosomal membranes; increasing binding at nanomolar concentrations and decreasing it at micromolar concentrations (5). Further studies demonstrated that this steroid may have mixed GABA-agonistic/antagonistic features because, whereas it slightly potentiates benzodiazepine binding, it also inhibits barbiturate-induced enhancement of benzodiazepine binding (15). Finally, GABA-antagonistic features of PS were deduced from the fact that PS, at low micromolar concentrations, competitively or pseudocompetitively inhibits binding of the convulsant [³⁵S]TBPS to the $GABA_A$-operated chloride channel and blocks GABA-induced chloride transport and current in synaptoneurosomes and neurons (IC_{50} = 20 to 60 µM) (15–17).

DHEAS also inhibits GABA-induced currents in neurons in a noncompetitive manner (IC_{50} about 10 µM) (19,20). In binding experiments DHEAS does not behave like PS; it slightly inhibits specific [³H]muscimol and [³H]flunitrazepam binding (at concentrations >100 µM), but it potently shifts dextrally the dose response curve for pentobarbital to enhance [³H]flunitrazepam binding (19).

The GABA-antagonistic features of PS, DHEAS and DHEA observed in vitro are consistent with the in vivo observations of their excitatory effects on neurons (21), and with their convulsant actions (22,23).

Although both PS and DHEAS inhibit GABA-induced currents, there are differences between these steroids in their modes, and presumably, sites of action. Whereas PS inhibits binding of the chloride channel ligands, [^{35}S]TBPS and [^{3}H]-1-phenyl-4-t-butyl-2,6,7-trioloxabicyclo-octane ([^{3}H]TBOB), DHEA does not (15,18). Also, DHEAS, unlike PS, does not enhance [^{3}H]benzodiazepine or [^{3}H]muscimol binding, but rather reduces them (20).

Interactions of Radiolabeled Neurosteroids with $GABA_A$ Receptors

[^{3}H]PS and [^{3}H]DHEAS bind specifically to at least two populations of sites in crude synaptosomal membranes from the rat brain. The populations of low-affinity and quite high-density binding sites for PS and DHEAS (K_d in the high-µM range; B_{max} >10 nmol/mg protein) may represent the loci of steroid incorporation into membrane lipids, whereas the populations of high- and intermediate-affinity binding sites for both steroids seem to be associated with $GABA_A$ receptors. The K_d of high-affinity PS binding sites is in the range of 300 to 500 nM, and the K_d of intermediate-affinity sites is about 20 µM. For DHEAS, the K_d of high-affinity sites is about 3 µM. PS and DHEAS inhibit each other's binding but their specific recognition sites seem distinct (18–20).

High-affinity binding sites for [^{3}H]PS and [^{3}H]DHEAS have different densities: the B_{max} for [^{3}H]PS binding (about 5 pmol/mg protein) is similar to the density of $GABA_A$ receptors, but the B_{max} for [^{3}H]DHEAS binding (about 60 pmol/mg protein) is much higher. [^{3}H]PS and [^{3}H]DHEAS binding sites also have different pharmacological profiles: [^{3}H]PS binding to high-affinity sites is inhibited by picrotoxin, and minimally inhibited by barbiturates (18), whereas binding of [^{3}H]DHEAS is robustly inhibited by barbiturates, but not by picrotoxin (19). These findings are consistent with the fact that PS, but not DHEAS, inhibits the binding of [^{35}S]TBPS or [^{3}H]TBOB (15,18), and suggest that the sites of action for PS may be the same as or proximal to those for convulsants, whereas DHEAS may act at sites close or identical to those where barbiturates act at the $GABA_A$ receptor. The populations of high-affinity [^{3}H]PS and [^{3}H]DHEAS binding sites in synaptosomal membranes also have distinct sensitivity to thermal denaturation and proteolytic digestion. Although PS binding seems resistant to both treatments, the high-affinity DHEAS binding sites are erased by these treatments. Treatment with phospholipase A_2 destroys all binding of both PS and DHEAS to synaptosomal membranes (18,20).

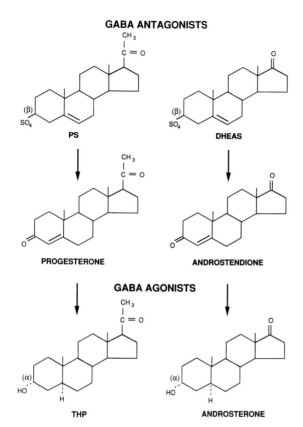

Figure 1. Structural and metabolic relationships between the GABA-antagonistic steroids PS and DHEAS and the GABA antagonistic steroids tetrahydroprogesterone and androsterone. PS and DHEAS can be converted to progesterone and androstenedione and subsequently reduced to THP and androsterone, respectively.

Based on our findings, we proposed that the high-affinity PS binding sites could be the hydrophobic pockets of the $GABA_A$ receptor protein, which are deeply embedded in the neuronal membrane and thus are insensitive to protein digestion. Alternatively, the PS binding sites may be the annular lipids intimately associated with the $GABA_A$ receptor. Theoretically, there should be one molecule of PS binding for each $GABA_A$ receptor, because densities of high-affinity PS binding sites and those of $GABA_A$ receptors are the same. In contrast, the high-affinity DHEAS binding sites seem to have a more defined proteinaceous nature, although binding to these sites also strongly depends on the phospholipid milieu.

Structural Relationships between GABA-Antagonistic and -Agonistic Steroids

A close metabolic link exists between GABA-antagonistic and -agonistic steroids, as shown in Figure 1. The GABA-antagonistic steroids, PS and

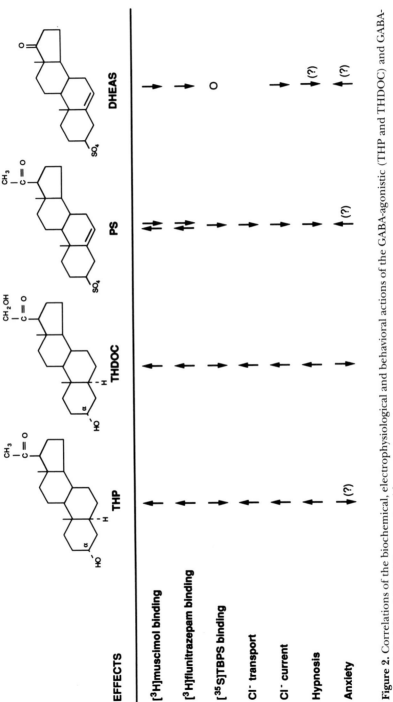

Figure 2. Correlations of the biochemical, electrophysiological and behavioral actions of the GABA-agonistic (THP and THDOC) and GABA-antagonistic (PS and DHEAS) neurosteroids.

DHEAS, formed in the CNS from cholesterol sulfate, can be desulfated by steroid sulfatases (24) and subsequently metabolized by brain enzymes to the GABA-agonistic steroids, THP and cis-androsterone. Such a metabolic link may be part of a homeostatic mechanism of control of neural activity through precise regulation of synthesis of counteracting neuromodulators.

Behavioral Effects of GABA-Modulatory Steroids

The GABA-agonistic features of THP and THDOC explain their hypnotic actions (25–28). These features also explain much earlier observations by Selye (29) of the rapid and reversible hypnotic effects of progesterone and deoxycorticosterone (precursors of THP and THDOC). Recently, anxiolytic effects of THDOC also were demonstrated in tests for anxiety in rodents (30) and THDOC, when tested in animal models for aggression, reduced the level of defeat-induced analgesia and increased the tendency of rodents to surrender in "resident-intruder" paradigms (31).

Hypnotic, anxiolytic and anesthetic actions of the GABA-agonistic steroids THP and THDOC contrast the behavioral effects of the GABA-antagonistic neurosteroid PS which, when injected intracerebroventricularly ($8 \mu g/10 \mu l$), reduced the pentobarbital-induced sleep time in rats (32). At lower doses, however, PS tended to prolong the sleep time. The neurosteroid DHEA, when injected intraperitoneally in doses from 100 to 150 mg/kg, produced tonic-clonic seizures in mice, but in lower doses caused behavioral sedation (23). The antianesthetic effects of PS and the convulsant actions of DHEA were most likely mediated via inhibition of $GABA_A$ receptors (15–17,19,20). Figure 2 summarizes biochemical, electrophysiological and behavioral actions of GABA-agonistic and GABA-antagonistic neurosteroids.

Summary

Bimodal regulation of the brain $GABA_A$ receptors by neurosteroids plays a role in the control of neuronal excitability, and as such may form the basis of a myriad of neurological and psychophysiological phenomena such as seizures, stress, anxiety, sleep, and depression. Therefore, aberrant synthesis of the neurosteroids may contribute to defects in neurotransmission and may result in various neural and affective disorders. These problems have been more fully discussed elsewhere (33,34).

References

1. Schofield PR, Darlison MG, Fujita N, et al. Sequence and functional expression of the GABA$_A$ receptor shows a ligand-gated receptor super-family. *Nature* 1987;328:221–227.
2. Olsen RW, Tobin AJ. Molecular biology of GABA$_A$ receptors. *FASEB J* 1990;4:1469–1480.
3. Vicini A. Pharmacologic significance of the structural heterogeneity of the GABA$_A$ receptor-chloride ion channel complex. *Neuropsychopharmacology* 1991;4:9–15.
4. Harrison NL, Simmonds MA. Modulation of GABA receptor complex by a steroid anesthetic. *Brain Res* 1984;323:284–293.
5. Majewska MD, Bisserbe JC, Eskay RE. Glucocorticoids are modulators of GABA$_A$ receptors in brain. *Brain Res* 1985;339:178–182.
6. Baulieu E-E, Robel P, Vatier O, et al. Neurosteroids: pregnenolone and dehydroepiandrosterone in the rat brain. In: Fuxe K, Agnati LF, eds. *Receptor-receptor interaction, a new intramembrane integrative mechanism.* Basingstoke: MacMillan, 1987;89–104.
7. Majewska MD, Harrison NL, Schwartz RD, et al. Steroid hormone metabolites are barbiturate-like modulators of the GABA receptor. *Science* 1986;232:1004–1007.
8. Harrison NL, Majewska MD, Harrington JW, et al. Structure-activity relationships for steroid interaction with the γ-aminobutyric acid$_A$ receptor complex. *J Pharmacol Exp Ther* 1987;241:346–353.
9. Lambert JJ, Peters JA, Cottrell GA. Actions of synthetic and endogenous steroids on the GABA$_A$ receptor. *Trends Pharmacol Sci* 1987;81:224–227.
10. Peters JA, Kirkness EF, Callachan H, et al. Modulation of the GABA$_A$ receptor by depressant barbiturates and pregnane steroids. *Brit J Pharmacol* 1988;94:1257–1269.
11. Turner DM, Ransom RW, Yang JS, et al. Steroid anesthetics and naturally occurring analogs modulate the γ-aminobutyric acid receptor complex at a site distinct from barbiturates. *J Pharmacol Exp Ther* 1989;248:960–966.
12. Majewska MD. Interaction of ethanol with the GABA$_A$ receptor in the rat brain: possible involvement of endogenous steroids. *Alcohol* 1988;5:269–273.
13. Lambert JJ, Peters JA, Sturgess NC, et al. Steroid modulation of the GABA$_A$ receptor complex: electrophysiological studies. *Ciba Found Symp* 1990;153:56–71.
14. Barker JL, Harrison NL, Lange GD, et al. Voltage-clamp studies of the potentiation of GABA-activated chloride conductance by the steroid anaesthetic alphaxalone and a reduced metabolite of progesterone in cultured rat C.N.S. *J Physiol (Lond)* 1986;377:83P.
15. Majewska MD, Schwartz RD. Pregnenolone-sulfate: an endogenous antagonist of the γ-aminobutyric acid receptor complex in brain? *Brain Res* 1987;404:355–360.
16. Majewska MD, Mienville JM, Vicini S. Neurosteroid pregnenolone sulfate antagonizes electrophysiological responses to GABA in neurons. *Neurosci Lett* 1988;90:279–284.
17. Mienville J-M, Vicini S. Pregnenolone sulfate antagonizes GABA$_A$ receptor-mediated currents via a reduction of channel opening frequency. *Brain Res* 1989;489:190–194.

18. Majewska MD, Demirgoren S, London ED. Binding of pregnenolone sulfate to rat brain membranes suggests multiple sites of steroid action at the GABA$_A$ receptor. *Eur J Pharmacol (Mol Pharmacol Sect)* 1990;189:307–315.
19. Majewska MD, Demirgoren S, Spivak ChE, et al. The neurosteroid dehydroepiandrosterone sulfate is an antagonist of the GABA$_A$ receptor. *Brain Res* 1990;526:143–146.
20. Demirgoren S, Majewska MD, Spivak Ch E, et al. Receptor binding and electrophysiological effects of dehydroepiandrosterone sulfate, an antagonist of the GABA$_A$ receptor. *Neuroscience* 1991;(in press).
21. Carette B, Poulain P. Excitatory effect of dehydroepiandrosterone, its sulphate ester and pregnenolone sulphate, applied by iontophoresis and pressure, on single neurons in the septo-optic area of the guinea pig. *Neurosci Lett* 1984;45:205–210.
22. Fidgor SK, Kodet MJ, Bloom BM, et al. Central activity and structure in a series of water soluble steroids. *J Pharmacol Exp Ther* 1957;119:299–309.
23. Heuser G, Ling GM, Buchwald NA. Sedation or seizures as dose-dependent effects of steroids. *Arch Neurol* 1965;13:195–203.
24. Iwamori M, Moser HW, Kishimoto Y. Steroid sulfatase in brain: comparison of sulfohydrolase activities for various steroid sulfates in normal and pathological brains, including various forms of metachromatic leukodystrophy. *J Neurochem* 1975;27:1389–1395.
25. Gyermek L, Iriarte J, Crabbe P. Steroids. CCCX. Structure-activity relationship of some steroidal hypnotic agents. *J Med Chem* 1968;11:117–125.
26. Kraulis I, Foldes G, Traikov H, et al. Distribution, metabolism and biological activity of deoxycorticosterone in the ventral nervous system. *Brain Res* 1975;88:1–14.
27. Holzbauer M. Physiological aspects of steroids with anaesthetic properties. *Med Biol* 1976;54:227–242.
28. Mendelson WB, Martin JV, Perlis M, et al. Sleep induction by adrenal steroid in the rat. *Psychopharmacology (Berlin)* 1987;93:226–229.
29. Selye H. Correlation between the chemical structure and the pharmacological actions of the steroids. *Endocrinology* 1942;39:437–452.
30. Crawley S, Glowa JR, Majewska MD, et al. Anxiolytic activity of endogenous adrenal steroid. *Brain Res* 1986;339:382–386.
31. Kavaliers M. Inhibitory influences of adrenal steroid, 3α,5α-tetrahydro-deoxycorticosterone on aggression and defeat-induced analgesia in mice. *Psychopharmacology (Berlin)* 1988;95:488–492.
32. Majewska MD, Bluet-Pajot M-T, Robel P, et al. Pregnenolone sulfate antagonizes barbiturate-induced sleep. *Pharmacol Biochem Behav* 1989;33:701–703.
33. Majewska MD. Steroids and brain activity. Essential dialogue between body and mind. *Biochem Pharmacol* 1987;36:3781–3788.
34. Majewska MD. Actions of steroids on neuron: role in personality, mood, stress, and disease. *Integrative Psychiatry* 1987;5:258–273.

Anionic Channel Regulation by Steroids

*Stefano Vicini, Ph.D., Giulia Puia, Ph.D., Giampaolo Mereu, Ph.D., *Peter H. Seeburg, Ph.D., and Erminio Costa, M.D.*

*Fidia-Georgetown Institute for the Neurosciences, Georgetown University School of Medicine, Washington, D.C. 20007; and *Center for Molecular Biology, University of Heidelberg, Heidelberg D6900, Germany*

The endogenous 3α-hydroxy ring A–reduced metabolites of progesterone and deoxycorticosterone interact potently with the γ-aminobutyric acid(GABA)–activated anionic channel in the CNS, and are termed neurosteroids (1). In particular, 3α-hydroxy-5α-pregnan-20-one (3α-OH-DHP) and 3α,21-dihydroxy-5α-pregnan-20-one (THDOC) at concentrations between 1 nM and 50 μM positively modulate GABA-activated Cl^- currents recorded in native membrane (1) as well as in reconstituted $GABA_A$ receptors (2,3). Furthermore, at concentrations of 1 μM or greater, these neurosteroids directly activate GABA-gated Cl^- channels in both native and recombinant $GABA_A$ receptors. Conversely, pregnenolone sulfate (PS, 3 to 50 μM) negatively modulates electrophysiological responses to GABA in neurons (4,5).

Glial cells in the CNS contain significant amounts of mitochondrial benzodiazepine receptors and mitochondrial cytochrome P-450, typical of steroidogenic tissues (for review see ref. 6). Moreover, de novo synthesis of several neurosteroids occurs directly in the CNS. These facts and the discovery of a variety of $GABA_A$ receptor subunits differentially expressed in the CNS (for review see refs. 7 and 8) have prompted the question of how specific neurosteroid biosynthesis and release in the CNS is regulated, and how steroids might be in modulating $GABA_A$ receptor subtypes.

Using electrophysiological means, we investigated the action of THDOC, 3α-OH-DHP and PS on diverse $GABA_A$ receptor subtypes transiently expressed in a tumoral cell line (transformed human embry-

119

onic kidney 293 cells, American Type Culture Collection #CRL 1573), as well as on postsynaptic $GABA_A$ receptors located at inhibitory synapses on CA1 pyramidal neurons of the hippocampus (details of the transfection methods can be found in ref. 2). In brief, the transient transfection was performed with the calcium phosphate precipitation technique, using 3 µg plasmid per 35-mm dish. One or more supercoiled plasmid $GABA_A$ receptor subunit cDNAs were singly inserted into $GABA_A$ receptor subunit cDNAs. Cultures of transfected cells were studied with the single-electrode voltage-clamp technique, in the whole-cell configuration (9) at room temperature on the stage of an inverted microscope. Cells were bathed in 145 mM NaCl, 5 mM KCl, 2 mM $CaCl_2$ and 5 mM HEPES-NaOH (pH 7.4). Recordings were made within 3 days of transfection. The recording pipette contained 145 mM CsCl, 1 mM $MgCl_2$, 11 mM EGTA and 10 mM HEPES-CsOH (pH 7.2). GABA (0.5 M in H_2O adjusted to pH 4 with HCl) was applied by iontophoresis with 30-msec pulses of positive current. With GABA iontophoretic currents in the 25- to 50-nA range, outward currents were generated in transfected cells in order to obtain a peak amplitude of 150 to 200 pA. Neurosteroids were a gift from Robert H. Purdy (Southwest Foundation for Medical Research, San Antonio, Texas), and were dissolved in bath solution containing dimethyl sulfoxide (DMSO) at a maximal final concentration of 0.01%. Drugs were applied by pressure (2 to 4 PSI) in the proximity of the cell body with micropipettes 5 to 10 µm in diameter. The application of DMSO (0.01% in bath medium) failed to modify GABA responses. Neurosteroids were applied for 5 sec between two GABA pulses delivered every 10 sec. The maximal Cl^- current measured from each cell was larger (>1 nA) than the test response of 150 to 200 pA we used, indicating that the percentages of potentiation observed were far below the maximal efficacy of the system. Current traces were recorded by a patch-clamp amplifier (EPC-7; List Electronics), filtered at 1,500 Hz (8-pole low-pass Bessel; Frequency Devices) and recorded on a chart recorder (Gould 2600S) for off-line analysis.

Hippocampal slices were prepared from Sprague-Dawley rats, at age 15 to 21 days. Thin (120 to 200 µm) slices were studied with the patch-clamp technique, as first described by Edwards and colleagues (10). Ringer solution contained the following (in mM): NaCl (120.0), KCl (3.1), Na_2HPO_4 (1.25), $NaHCO_3$ (26.0), dextrose (5.0), $MgCl_2$ (1.0) and $CaCl_2$ (2.0). The solution was maintained at pH 7.4 by bubbling with 5% $CO_2 + 95\%$ O_2 and was perfused over the slice at a rate of 5 ml/min. Patch pipettes were filled with the following (in mM): Cs-gluconate (145.0),

Table 1. Neurosteroids modulate recombinant GABA$_A$ receptors

GABA Receptor Subunit Combination	Pregnenolone Sulfate 10 μM	3α-OH-DHP 1 μM
β1	−26 ± 7 (3)	210 ± 70 (6)
α1β1	−39 ± 7 (4)	373 ± 75 (4)
α1β1γ2	−25 ± 8 (5)	218 ± 70 (4)
α2β1γ2	−25 ± 5 (8)	NT
α3β1γ2	−39 ± 7 (4)	250 ± 80 (7)
α5β1γ2	−40 ± 5 (6)	172 ± 30 (3)
α1β1γ1	−27 ± 8 (6)	226 ± 70 (6)

Neurosteroid effects expressed in percent potentiation of GABA-activated Cl⁻ currents with respect to control. Values expressed as mean ± SEM of (N) cells tested. The percent potentiation by 3α-OH-DHP was not statistically different among the various combinations tested ($p < 0.05$). NT, not tested.

MgCl$_2$ (1.0), EGTA (5.0), ATP (2.0) and HEPES-CsOH (10.0) to pH 7.2. Neurosteroids were applied to the recording chamber through a system of parallel inputs. Stimuli (square-wave electric pulses of 100- to 300-μA intensity, 50-μsec duration and 0.3-Hz frequency) were delivered to the Schaffer collateral pathway to CA1 neurons through concentric electrodes positioned 200 to 500 μm distal to the recorded cell. By voltage-clamping the neuron at 0 mV, the excitatory synaptic currents obtained were close to reversal potential, and pure inhibitory postsynaptic currents (IPSCs) were recorded. Stimulus intensity was adjusted to obtain a 60% of maximal response, and then was maintained at a constant level. Kinetics and amplitudes of IPSCs were analyzed by computer-assisted semiautomated procedures with single or double exponential equations (11). A sample of 20 to 30 IPSCs during the control period, during THDOC perfusion, and 10 min after washout were recorded and averaged for comparison.

Table 1 shows a comparison of the positive and negative modulation of GABA-activated currents by neurosteroids in transfected cells with different subunit combinations. These results show that changing the molecular structure of the GABA$_A$ receptor in terms of constituting subunit combinations has little or no effect on the action of both PS and 3α-OH-DHP. The data in Table 1 also indicate clearly that the presence of γ1 or γ2 subunits is not required for the expression of positive or negative modulation by neurosteroids, and their potency and quality of modulation fails to change if either of the subunits is present. It also was important to determine if neurosteroids were able to modulate GABA receptors located in postsynaptic densities in a given area of the CNS. Therefore, we present preliminary results on the modulation by THDOC of transsynaptically elicited GABA currents (IPSCs) recorded from hippocampal CA1 neurons in rat brain slices. Bath application of THDOC (1 µM) potentiated both the amplitude and the decay time constant of IPSCs recorded from CA1 pyramidal neurons. The average IPSC amplitude recorded in 15 CA1 neurons was 175 ± 32 pA (mean $\pm$ SD) and became 215 ± 23 pA (mean $\pm$ SD) in the presence of THDOC, with no statistically significant variation elicited by the drug. In contrast, THDOC potently prolonged the duration of IPSCs, and the average decay time constant changed from 42 ± 15 msec (mean $\pm$ SD) to 315 ± 63 msec (mean $\pm$ SD) in the presence of THDOC ($p<0.01$, Student's t test for group values). These results clearly show an action of neurosteroids on native $GABA_A$ receptors in the hippocampal slice, of comparable intensity to that observed in recombinant receptors.

In conclusion, our results indicate that neurosteroids act with high affinity and potent efficacy on native and recombinant $GABA_A$ receptors, and show a pharmacological profile much less differentiated than benzodiazepines (12) relative to the molecular composition of the receptor. This profile of action clearly distinguishes neurosteroids from benzodiazepines, thus having profound implications for the regulation of the $GABA_A$ receptors. Assuming that physiological stimuli use the release and increased synthesis of neurosteroids to regulate $GABA_A$ receptor function, variation of their release could have an important role in the pathogenesis of a variety of diseases affecting GABAergic synaptic transmission. Furthermore, understanding the CNS endogenous production of these and other related neurosteroids may provide a means for developing new potent and selective pharmacological tools. Such tools could be used in the treatment of the behavioral and neurological disorders that result from the defective or excessive production of neurosteroids regulating GABA action at $GABA_A$ receptors.

References

1. Majewska MD, Harrison NL, Schwartz RD, et al. Steroid hormone metabolites are barbiturate-like modulators of the GABA receptor. *Science* 1986;232:1004–1007.
2. Puia G, Santi MR, Vicini S, et al. Neurosteroids act on recombinant human $GABA_A$ receptors. *Neuron* 1990;4:759–765.
3. Shingai R, Sutherland ML, Barnard EA. Effects of subunit types of the cloned $GABA_A$ receptor on the response to a neurosteroid. *Eur J Pharmacol* 1991; 206:77–80.

4. Majewska MD, Mienville JM, Vicini S. Neurosteroid pregnenolone-sulfate antagonizes electrophysiological responses to GABA in neurons. *Neurosci Lett* 1988; 90:279–284.

5. Mienville JM, Vicini S. Pregnenolone sulfate antagonizes $GABA_A$ receptor-mediated currents via a reduction of channel opening frequency. *Brain Res* 1989; 489:190–194.

6. Krueger KE. Peripheral-type benzodiazepine receptors: a second site of action for benzodiazepines. *Neuropsychopharmacology* 1991;4:237–244.

7. Vicini S. Pharmacological significance of the structural heterogeneity of the $GABA_A$ receptor-chloride ion channel complex. *Neuropsychopharmacology* 1991; 4:9–15.

8. Olsen RW, Tobin AJ. Molecular biology of $GABA_A$ receptors. *FASEB J* 1990;4:1469–1480.

9. Hamill OP, Marty A, Neher E, et al. Improved patch-clamp techniques for high-resolution current recording from cells and cell-free membrane patches. *Pflügers Arch* 1981;391:85–100.

10. Edwards FA, Konnerth A, Sakmann B, et al. A thin slice preparation for patch clamp recordings from synaptically connected neurones of mammalian central nervous system. *Pflügers Arch* 1989;414:600–612.

11. Vicini S, Schuetze SM. Gating properties of acetylcholine receptors at developing rat endplates. *J Neurosci* 1985;5:2212–2224.

12. Puia G, Vicini S, Seeburg PH, et al. Influence of recombinant $GABA_A$ receptor subunit composition on the action of allosteric modulators of GABA-gated Cl^- currents. *Mol Pharmacol* 1991;36:691–696.

Corticosteroid Receptor in Neuronal Membranes Associated with Rapid Suppression of Sexual Behavior

*Miles Orchinik, *Thomas F. Murray, Ph.D.,*
and Frank L. Moore, Ph.D.

*Department of Zoology, *Department of Pharmacy, Oregon State University,*
Corvallis, Oregon 97331

Clearly, the traditional model of steroid hormone action, involving activation of intracellular steroid receptors that regulate gene expression, cannot account for all the steroid effects on brain function (1). Steroid modulation of neuronal excitability (2–4), of neuronal responses to amino acid transmitters (5,6), and of neuropeptide receptors (7) are examples of steroid actions that appear to occur independently of classic intracellular receptors. For example, these responses are evoked within seconds of steroid administration, in brain regions lacking classic intracellular steroid receptors, when access to intracellular receptors or when gene transcription is blocked. These types of responses to steroids could be explained by specific receptors for steroids on neuronal membranes. Towle and Sze (8) found low-affinity binding sites for adrenal and gonadal steroids on neuronal membranes. Subsequent studies found low-affinity binding of the neurosteroid [^{3}H]dehydroepiandrosterone sulfate (9) and high-affinity binding of progesterone complexed to iodinated bovine serum albumin (10) in neuronal membranes. We recently found, as described in this chapter, a high-affinity binding site for corticosterone (CORT) in synaptic membranes from an amphibian brain, with the characteristics of a bona fide receptor (11). This corticosteroid receptor on neuronal membranes has a unique pharmacological specificity and appears physiologically relevant, controlling rapid behavioral responses to stress.

We initiated our studies in *Taricha granulosa,* the rough-skinned newt, to determine the mechanism responsible for the suppression of male sexual behavior by short-term stress. The response to stress depends on the adrenal (interrenal) steroid CORT and is mimicked by CORT injection (12,13). Because the inhibition of sex behavior after stress or CORT injection occurred within minutes rather than hours, we hypothesized that this behavioral response is mediated by corticosteroid receptors on neuronal membranes.

We performed radioligand binding studies to test this hypothesis using an extensively washed P_2 neuronal membrane preparation from whole *Taricha* brains, separating receptor-bound from free [^{3}H]CORT by vacuum filtration. Under these conditions, measurement of [^{3}H]CORT binding to soluble intracellular receptors should be minimal. We found that the binding of [^{3}H]CORT to this preparation was specific, saturable and of high affinity; the equilibrium binding parameters were estimated as $K_d = 0.51$ nM and $B_{max} = 146$ fmol/mg protein. The binding affinity was comparable to the affinity of CORT for brain intracellular adrenal steroid receptors (14,15), but markedly different from the low-affinity ($K_d = 120$ nM) CORT binding site on synaptic membranes described by Towle and Sze (8). Kinetic experiments indicated that the association of [^{3}H]CORT with membranes was relatively rapid and completely reversible. The K_d value calculated from kinetic data approximated the K_d estimated from equilibrium saturation data. These data satisfy important criteria in validating the radioligand-binding assay methodology.

The validity of the assay was further supported by experiments showing that [^{3}H]CORT-specific binding was temperature sensitive—greatest at 30°C, but eliminated by heating to 60°C. Specific binding also was inhibited in a concentration-dependent manner by treatment with the protease trypsin. These data suggest that [^{3}H]CORT binds to a receptor-like protein in the P_2 fraction.

Using more purified subcellular fractions prepared by discontinuous sucrose gradient centrifugation, we found that the [^{3}H]CORT recognition sites were localized in synaptic membranes. The specific binding activity of [^{3}H]CORT was most enriched (more than 11-fold) in the synaptic membrane fraction, compared with binding activity in brain homogenates. Furthermore, the enrichment of [^{3}H]CORT binding in the synaptosomal fraction precisely paralleled the enrichment of quinuclidinyl benzilate ([^{3}H]QNB, a muscarinic cholinergic receptor ligand used as a marker for synaptic membranes) binding. In contrast, the binding of [^{3}H]CORT to the nuclear and cytosolic fractions was negligible under the conditions of this assay. Because intracellular adrenal steroid receptors are localized in the nuclear and cytosolic fractions, but binding there is minimal, these data provide further evidence that [³H]CORT binding in the synaptic membrane fraction is not because of contamination by intracellular receptors.

Competition experiments indicated that the recognition site was highly specific for CORT, and the ligand binding specificity did not resemble that of the intracellular adrenal steroid receptors in either mammals (14,15) or amphibians (16,17). Other than cortisol, none of the Type I or Type II corticoid receptor ligands tested, including aldosterone and dexamethasone, displayed high affinity for this site. The gonadal steroids tested also were poor competitors for the [³H]CORT binding site. Interestingly, electrophysiological studies suggest that there may be membrane-bound corticosteroid receptors on mammalian neurons that are also insensitive to both aldosterone and dexamethasone (18).

By exploiting the pharmacological specificity of this binding site, we were able to visualize [³H]CORT binding sites in *Taricha* brains by using in vitro receptor autoradiography. Brain sections were incubated with [³H]CORT in a buffer containing 200 nM ZK91587 and dexamethasone to occupy intracellular corticoid receptors. Specific binding sites detected under these conditions were located almost exclusively in regions of neuropil, areas rich in synaptic terminals, rather than over perikarya where intracellular steroid receptors are localized. This distribution of [³H]CORT binding sites provides corroborating evidence for the presence of CORT binding sites on synaptic membranes. The binding sites were found in brain regions known to play a role in regulating sexual behavior, including the amygdala, preoptic area and hypothalamus.

Do these membrane-associated recognition sites represent functional, behaviorally relevant receptors? Recent data obtained from microelectrode recordings from *Taricha* brains are consistent with membrane receptor–mediated changes in neuronal excitability induced by CORT: the antidromic spike amplitude of hindbrain neurons was consistently altered within 2 min of CORT application (19). To address this question behaviorally, we obtained dose-response curves for the rapid suppression of male sexual behavior by CORT and other corticoids with known affinities for the [³H]CORT recognition site. Courtship behavior of male *Taricha* involves the amplectic clasping of a female newt until the female displays receptive behavior. This clasping behavior is inhibited by stress (12). The behavior was rapidly suppressed—within 8 min—by intraperitoneal (i.p.) injection of CORT, relative to saline-injected controls. Also,

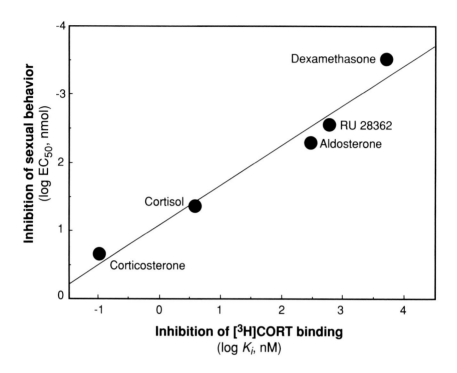

Figure 1. Linear relationship between potency of steroids in inhibition of [³H]CORT binding and potency in inhibition of sexual behavior. Males were injected i.p. with one of 5 to 7 doses of steroid or vehicle (in most cases, n = 24 for each dose of steroid). Females were added to tanks 5 min after injection, when behavioral testing was initiated. Data recorded as number of claspers within 20 min. [©1991 by the AAAS. Reprinted with permission from ref. 11.]

behavior was significantly inhibited after injection of as little as 2.5 nmol CORT. The rapidity of the response and the sensitivity to CORT are consistent with the presence of high-affinity CORT receptors on synaptic membranes. A linear relationship was displayed (Figure 1) between the potencies of the 5 corticoids tested in inhibiting sexual behavior and their potencies to inhibit [³H]CORT binding ($R^2 = 0.96$; $P < 0.005$). This strong correlation suggests that the membrane-bound CORT recognition site plays a role in the regulation of behavior.

Several lines of evidence imply that [³H]CORT binding in the membrane fraction represents a functional receptor that may mediate stress-induced inhibition of sexual behavior. Equilibrium saturation binding, kinetic data and control experiments are consistent with a ligand-receptor interaction. The subcellular localization of [³H]CORT binding activity in the synaptic membrane fraction and the autoradiographical distribution of [3H]CORT binding sites in the neuropil suggest that corticosteroid receptors are present on synaptic membranes. Such a presence could account for the rapidity of the electrophysiological and behavioral responses to CORT. Finally, the affinities of steroids for the [3H]CORT binding site are strongly correlated with their potencies to modulate sexual behavior.

Perhaps the most elegant evidence for steroid interaction with neuronal membranes is the steroid modulation of the γ-aminobutyric acid(GABA)$_A$ receptor (5,20,21). The GABA$_A$ receptor/chloride channel is a complex macromolecule with a multiplicity of allosterically interacting binding sites. We examined the possibility that the CORT recognition site in *Taricha* brains is associated with the GABA$_A$ receptor. However, evidence indicates that the CORT receptor and the GABA$_A$ receptor are independent. We found that the potencies of steroids to alter GABA$_A$ receptor ligand binding in *Taricha* brains were similar to potencies reported for the rat (5,20). Nanomolar concentrations of the adrenal and gonadal steroid metabolites, 5α-pregnan-3α,21-diol-20-one (5α-THDOC) and 5α-pregnane-3α-ol-20-one (3α-OH-DHP), inhibited binding of the chloride channel antagonist t-butyl-bicyclophosphorothionate ([35S]TBPS), whereas CORT was a far less potent competitor. Similarly, the binding of the benzodiazepine [3H]flunitrazepam was enhanced by 5α-THDOC, but CORT had minimal efficacy. Consistent with the low potency of CORT to alter GABA$_A$ ligand binding, CORT had no effect on GABA-stimulated $^{36}Cl^-$ flux into *Taricha* synaptoneurosomes. In the rodent brain as well, CORT does not enhance GABA-stimulated $^{36}Cl^-$ flux (22).

Consistent with these results, GABA$_A$ receptor agonists and antagonists, specific for the GABA, benzodiazepine, barbiturate and chloride channel sites, were ineffective at displacing [3H]CORT binding to membranes. The most potent GABA$_A$ ligand was the benzodiazepine diazepam, which inhibited [3H]CORT binding with only low micromolar affinity. The deoxycorticosterone metabolite, 5α-THDOC, inhibited [3H]CORT binding with modest affinity (K_i = 297 nM), but 3α-OH-DHP was devoid of activity. In behavior experiments, injections of up to 100 nmol of either 5α-THDOC or 3α-OH-DHP failed to inhibit *Taricha* sexual behavior. These data indicate that the steroid modulation of GABA$_A$ receptors may have been highly conserved throughout vertebrate evolution, but also that the membrane-bound CORT receptor is not associated with the GABA$_A$ receptor.

We screened a number of other neurotransmitter ligands for activity at the CORT receptor, including agonists and antagonists for *N*-methyl-D-aspartate, dopamine, acetylcholine and serotonin receptors. None of the ligands tested displayed high affinity for the [^{3}H]CORT binding site.

Many hormone and neurotransmitter receptors belong to a family of proteins that use G proteins for signal transduction (23). The CORT receptor also appears to be a G protein–coupled receptor. One characteristic of receptors that couple to G proteins is that the binding of an agonist to the receptor facilitates the exchange of GTP for GDP. The binding of GTP in turn shifts the receptor from a high-affinity to a low-affinity state for agonist binding. In binding studies, this process is reflected in a concentration-dependent inhibition of agonist binding by GTP or nonhydrolyzable analogues of GTP (24,25). The CORT recognition site of *Taricha* brain membranes displays similar characteristics (26). Specific binding of [^{3}H]CORT was inhibited up to 85% in a concentration-dependent manner by guanine nucleotides. The rank order potency of nucleotides to inhibit [^{3}H]CORT binding was guanosine 5'-O-(3-thiotriphosphate) (GTP-γS) > 5'-guanylylimidodiphosphate > GDP $\geq$ GTP>ATP. In addition, GTP-γS induced a rapid component of [^{3}H]CORT dissociation (k_{-1} increased > 20-fold) from neuronal membranes. Similar to other G protein–coupled receptors, the addition of Mg^{2+} to EDTA-treated membranes enhanced [^{3}H]CORT binding in a concentration-dependent manner, and Mg^{2+} enhanced the potency of guanine nucleotides to inhibit [^{3}H]CORT binding.

Therefore, the transduction mechanism associated with the CORT membrane receptor appears to involve a G protein. A similar G protein–coupled steroid receptor likely mediates the rapid, cAMP-dependent changes in neuronal excitability induced by estradiol (4,27). The latency of neuronal responses to CORT is consistent with G protein–mediated transmembrane signaling. Direct steroid regulation of ion channels occurs with a latency of seconds, whereas most steroid-directed changes in protein synthesis occur with a latency of hours. In contrast with these mechanisms, application of CORT to *Taricha* neurons alters membrane excitability within 2 min (19), similar to the response latency of certain mammalian neurons to CORT administration (3,18).

Steroids, like most neuromodulators, appear to use multiple receptor subtypes, transduction mechanisms and effector systems. Our data indicate that corticosteroids can alter brain function through a novel mechanism—by binding to a G protein–coupled receptor on neuronal membranes. Given the conservation of steroid hormones and receptors across vertebrate evolution, similar receptors are probably common to many vertebrate species. Inasmuch as these CORT receptors appear to regulate behavioral responses to stress in *Taricha*, these studies may contribute to our understanding of stress-related behavioral and/or affective disorders.

References

1. McEwen BS, Coirini H, Schumacher M. Steroid effects on neuronal activity: when is the genome involved? *Ciba Found Symp* 1990;153:3–21.
2. Kelly MJ, Moss RL, Dudley CA. The effects of microelectrophoretically applied estrogen, cortisol, and acetylcholine on medial preoptic septal unit activity throughout the estrous cycle of the female rat. *Exp Brain Res* 1977;30:53–64.
3. Hua SY, Chen YZ. Membrane receptor-mediated electrophysiological effects of glucocorticoid on mammalian neurons. *Endocrinology* 1989;124:687–691.
4. Nabekura J, Oomura Y, Minami T, et al. Mechanism of the rapid effect of 17B-estradiol on medial amygdala neurons. *Science* 1986;233:226–228.
5. Majewska MD, Harrison NL, Schwartz RD, et al. Steroid hormone metabolites are barbiturate-like modulators of the GABA receptor. *Science* 1986;232:1004–1007.
6. Smith SS, Waterhouse BD, Woodward DJ. Sex steroid effects on extrahypothalamic CNS. I. Estrogen augments neuronal responsiveness to iontophoretically applied glutamate in the cerebellum. *Brain Res* 1987;422:40–51.
7. Schumacher M, Coirini H, Pfaff DW, et al. Behavioral effects of progesterone associated with rapid modulation of oxytocin receptors. *Science* 1990;250:691–694.
8. Towle AC, Sze PY. Steroid binding to synaptic plasma membrane: differential binding of glucocorticoids and gonadal steroids. *J Steroid Biochem* 1983;18:135–143.
9. Majewska MD, Demirgoren S, Spivak CE, et al. The neurosteroid dehydroepiandrosterone sulfate is an allosteric antagonist of the $GABA_A$ receptor. *Brain Res* 1990;526:143–146.
10. Ke F-C, Ramirez VD. Binding of progesterone to nerve cell membranes of rat brain using progesterone conjugated to ^{125}I-bovine serum albumin as a ligand. *J Neurochem* 1990;54:467–472.
11. Orchinik M, Murray TF, Moore FL. A corticosteroid receptor in neuronal membranes. *Science* 1991;252:1848–1851.
12. Moore FL, Miller LJ. Stress-induced inhibition of sexual behavior: corticosterone inhibits courtship behaviors of a male amphibian (*Taricha granulosa*). *Horm Behav* 1984;18:400–410.
13. Boyd SK, Moore FL. Evidence for GABA involvement in stress-induced inhibition of male amphibian sexual behavior. *Horm Behav* 1990;24:128–138.
14. McEwen BS, De Kloet ER, Rostene W. Adrenal steroid receptors and actions in the nervous system. *Physiol Rev* 1986;66:1121–1188.
15. De Kloet ER, Reul JMHM. Feedback action and tonic influence of corticosteroids on brain function: a concept arising from the heterogeneity of brain receptor systems. *Psychoneuroendocrinology* 1987;12:83–105.

16. Medhi AZ, DiBattista JA, Sandor T. Glucocorticoid receptors of the American bullfrog (*Rana catesbeiana*). *Gen Comp Endocrinol* 1984;53:475.

17. Lange CB, Hanke W. Corticosteroid receptors in liver cytosol of the clawed toad, *Xenopus lævis:* daily and seasonal variations. *Gen Comp Endocrinol* 1988;71:141–152.

18. Chen YZ, Hua SY, Wang CA, et al. An electrophysiological study on the membrane receptor-mediated action of glucocorticoids in mammalian neurons. *Neuroendocrinology* 1991;53(Suppl 1):25–30.

19. Rose JD, Moore FL, Orchinik M. Rapid neurophysiological actions of corticosterone related to stress-induced inhibition of sexual behavior in an amphibian. *Soc Neurosci Abstr* 1991;(in press).

20. Gee KW. Steroid modulation of the GABA/benzodiazepine receptor-linked chloride ionophore. *Mol Neurobiol* 1988;2:291–317.

21. Puia G, Santi M, Vicini S, et al. Neurosteroids act on recombinant human $GABA_A$ receptors. *Neuron* 1990;4:759–765.

22. Morrow AL, Pace JR, Purdy RH, et al. Characterization of steroid interactions with gamma-aminobutyric acid receptor-gated chloride ion channels: evidence for multiple steroid recognition sites. *Mol Pharmacol* 1990;37:263–270.

23. Bourne HR, Sanders DA, McCormick F. The GTPase superfamily: conserved structure and molecular mechanism. *Nature* 1991;349:117–127.

24. Gilman AG. G Proteins: transducers of receptor-generated signals. *Annu Rev Biochem* 1987;56:615–649.

25. Birnbaumer L. G Proteins in signal transduction. *Annu Rev Pharmacol Toxicol* 1990;30:675–705.

26. Orchinik M, Murray TF, Moore FL. Membrane bound corticosteroid receptor is coupled to a G protein. *Soc Neurosci Abstr* 1991;(in press).

27. Minami T, Oomura Y, Nabekura J, et al. 17β-Estradiol depolarization of hypothalamic neurons is mediated by cyclic AMP. *Brain Res* 1990;519:301–307.

V

Recent Studies on the Regulation of Steroid Synthesis in the Brain and Periphery

Metabolism of Progesterone and Related Steroids by Neural and Neuroendocrine Structures

Harry J. Karavolas, Ph.D., and Donald R. Hodges

Department of Physiological Chemistry, University of Wisconsin, Madison, Wisconsin 53706

The metabolic processing of neuroactive steroids such as progesterone appears to be an important component of the cellular mechanisms by which these steroids achieve their various neural and neuroendocrine effects (1). In mammalian neural and neuroendocrine structures, this processing of progesterone and related steroids such as 20α-dihydroprogesterone and 17α-hydroxyprogesterone is primarily a reductive process involving the C-4,5 double bond and the C-3 and C-20 ketones. The formation of these reduced metabolites in pituitary and neural tissues appears to be a means by which the parent steroid (progesterone or a similar steroid) can be made into more active, less active, or inactive forms (1,2). The diverse effects of progesterone and related steroids can result from the actions of the parent steroid itself or from one or more specific metabolites.

In this chapter we summarize our findings on the characteristics of the neural and pituitary metabolism of progesterone and the other major ovarian progestins, 20α-dihydroprogesterone and 17α-hydroxyprogesterone, especially in the hypothalamus and anterior pituitary of female rats. We also discuss the nature of the metabolites, their relationship to progesterone's effects, tissue differences in metabolism, the effects of different physiological states, and some characteristics of the principal metabolizing enzymes. Finally, we consider how these ubiquitous metabolic steps can generate specific target tissue responses.

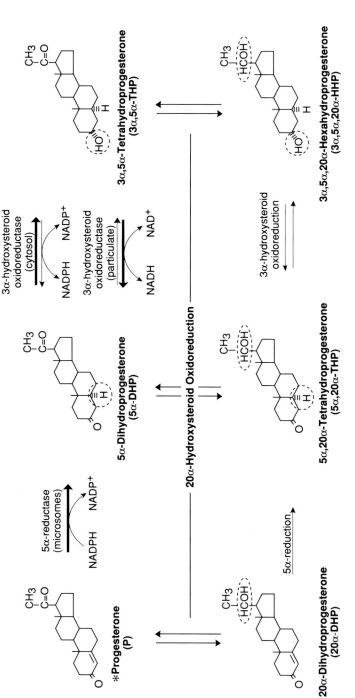

Figure 1. Major and Minor Metabolic Pathways for the Neural and Pituitary Processing of Progesterone. The major pathway, denoted by *bold arrows* (**top half**), is through 5α-DHP and $3\alpha,5\alpha$-THP. *In our studies, there was neither evidence of any 17α-hydroxylation to suggest a metabolic pathway to C_{19} products when 17α-hydroxyprogesterone was used as substrate (see text for details).

Nature of Metabolites and Metabolic Pathways

Progesterone Metabolism

Using in vitro and in vivo studies and reverse isotopic dilution analyses, we identified and measured the metabolites formed in several female rat neural and neuroendocrine structures, including the anterior pituitary, hypothalamus, midbrain-tectum, cerebral cortex, thalamus, tegmentum, medulla, cerebellum and pineal (1–3). In these tissues, especially in the pituitary and the hypothalamus, the major metabolites of progesterone were usually 5α-dihydroprogesterone and 3α,5α-tetrahydroprogesterone (Figure 1, top half), indicating substantial progesterone 5α-reductase and 3α-hydroxysteroid oxidoreductase (3α-HSOR) activity. Generally, we found minor amounts of the corresponding 20α-reduced metabolites, 20α-dihydroprogesterone, 5α,20α-tetrahydroprogesterone and 3α,5α,20α-hexahydroprogesterone, indicating some 20α-hydroxysteroid oxidoreductase activity (Figure 1, bottom). Other investigators have reported similar conversions of progesterone to 5α-, 3α-, and 20α-reduced metabolites by brain and pituitary tissues of female and male rats, and other species such as chickens, guinea pigs, dogs, monkeys and humans (1,4,5).

5β- and 3β-Isomers and Other Metabolites

There was no definitive evidence for 3β-, 5β-, or 20β-reduced isomers in our studies, although other investigators have reported 3β- and 5β-reduced products for chickens and dogs (1,5). Using reverse isotopic dilution analyses and separation systems that distinguish α and β isomers, significant radioactivity was associated only with the 5α-, 3α-, and 20α-reduced derivatives. However, because the radioactivity occasionally associated with carrier 3β-, 5β-, and 20β-compounds was too low for meaningful analysis, that possibility remains. If these metabolites were present, they could not have been more than a trace of the metabolized radioactivity (<0.05%). Other derivatives may have been present because in some incubations small amounts of unidentified radioactivity (usually 1% to 5%) were associated with thin-layer chromatography zones corresponding to more polar compounds, probably hydroxylated metabolites, but not 17α-hydroxyprogesterone.

Pituitary and Hypothalamic Metabolism of 20α-Dihydroprogesterone and 17α-Hydroxyprogesterone

When 20α-dihydroprogesterone was used as substrate with the female rat hypothalamus and pituitary, we observed similar conversions (2). The pathway is essentially that shown in the lower half of Figure 1. We detected no appreciable conversion to progesterone (<1%). The major metabolites were the corresponding 5α- and 3α-reduced derivatives: 5α,20α-tetrahydroprogesterone and 3α,5α,20α-hexahydroprogesterone. With 17α-hydroxyprogesterone, we found conversions analogous to those obtained with progesterone (Figure 1). The major products in both tissues were 17α-hydroxy-5α-pregnane-3,20-dione and 3α,17α-dihydroxy-5α-pregnan-20-one, with small amounts of the corresponding 20α-reduced products (6).

Is There Conversion of Progesterone or 17α-Hydroxyprogesterone to C_{19} Products?

In the studies on progesterone metabolism, there was no evidence of any 17α-hydroxylation to suggest a pathway to C_{19} steroids. In the 17α-hydroxyprogesterone study, the presence of the 17α-hydroxy moiety offered the possibility that we might observe side-chain cleavage to C_{19} products. Because certain brain structures, including the hypothalamus, can convert certain C_{19} androgens to estrogens, there also was the possibility of in situ aromatization (1,7). However, with both the pituitary and hypothalamus, there was no evidence for the formation of C_{19} metabolites (testosterone, androstenedione, 5α-dihydrotestosterone, and 5α-androstane-3α,17β-diol) (6). Thus, with the three major ovarian progestins as substrates, the principal progestin-metabolizing activities in the tissues examined were 5α- and 3α-reduction with minor amounts of 20α-reduction (1).

Active or Inactive Derivatives?

Some of these reduced derivatives are inactive, have variable effects, or share some of the biological responses traditionally associated with progesterone, especially neuroendocrine effects (1). For example, 5α-dihydroprogesterone and 3α,5α-tetrahydroprogesterone do not affect uterine progestational parameters but have neuroendocrine effects on gonadotropin regulation and sexual behavior. Some metabolites such as 3α,5α-tetrahydroprogesterone have potent neural and neuroendocrine effects and may be the active intermediaries in some neural processes. Of course, 3α,5α-tetrahydroprogesterone is a potent anesthetic, antiepileptic and barbiturate-like modulator of the γ-aminobutyric acid (GABA) receptor complex (8).

Tissue Differences in Processing Progesterone

Quantitative or qualitative tissue differences in the production of metabolites that are more active, less active, or retain only certain effects of the parent steroid can be important in regulating the neuroactive effects of progesterone and related steroids. If so, there might be changes in the metabolic processing of progesterone among various target and nontarget tissues or with changing physiological states (e.g., estrous cycle, pregnancy, or reproductive senescence).

In Vitro Studies

Among the pituitary and brain tissues examined, quantitative but no apparent qualitative differences were found in the metabolism of progesterone (1,9). Although progesterone 5α- and 3α-reduction and some 20α-reduction are common properties of these tissues, there were differences in the relative levels of 3α-, 5α-, and 20α-reduced products formed (1). Highest levels of 5α-dihydroprogesterone formation occurred in the pituitary (30% to 35%) followed by the hypothalamus and medulla (18% to 22%), and by the thalamus, midbrain-tectum, tegmentum and cerebellum (10% to 12%). The pineal had the lowest levels (<1%). Levels of 3α,5α-tetrahydroprogesterone were highest in the pituitary and hypothalamus (11% to 15%) followed by the cerebellum (4%), and by the thalamus, midbrain-tectum, tegmentum and medulla (1% to 2%). The pineal again was lowest (<1%). Minor amounts of 20α-reduced metabolites were formed. Highest levels were in the pineal and cerebellum (0.1%) and lowest in the pituitary and hypothalamus (<0.05%), with intermediate amounts in the other tissues (0.05% to 0.08%). Regarding the localization of these activities within the pituitary and hypothalamus, we and other investigators found that progesterone 5α- and 3α-reduction are enriched in progesterone target areas such as gonadotropes and median eminence (4,10–12).

In Vivo Studies

We also observed in vivo differences among various neural and neuroendocrine structures in the steroidal compounds that were selectively accumulated above plasma and nontarget tissue levels after injection of [³H]progesterone into ovariectomized or estrogen-treated ovariectomized rats (13). Most of the accumulated tissue radioactivity was associated not with the original [³H]steroid but with the metabolites of progesterone shown in Figure 1. 5α-Dihydroprogesterone was the predominant

[³H]steroid in the pituitary, and was the other major [³H]steroid besides progesterone in neural tissues other than the pineal. There were large selective accumulations of 5α-dihydroprogesterone by the pituitary and hypothalamus, followed by the midbrain-tectum and cerebellum. Lesser amounts of 3α,5α-tetrahydroprogesterone were found, with selective accumulations only in the pituitary and pineal. Estrogen treatment increased accumulations of progesterone and certain metabolites only in the pineal and midbrain-tectum. Tissue levels of other metabolites were generally not different from nontarget tissues. When [³H]-5α-dihydroprogesterone was similarly injected, it was the predominant [³H]steroid in the pituitary, hypothalamus and pineal, but 3α,5α-tetrahydroprogesterone predominated in the midbrain-tectum. Selective accumulations of 5α-dihydroprogesterone were observed in the pituitary, hypothalamus and midbrain-tectum.

Pituitary and Hypothalamic Metabolism of Progesterone During Changing Physiological States

Rat pituitary and hypothalamic 5α- and 3α-reduction of progesterone fluctuate over the estrous cycle (3). We observed changes in pituitary but not hypothalamic progesterone 5α-reduction during different stages of pregnancy (14). Formation of 5α-dihydroprogesterone was lower on days 15 and 21 of pregnancy than on day 1. Progesterone metabolism also was quantitatively different in the pituitaries (but not the hypothalami) of aged rats during three stages of reproductive aging (constant estrus, repeated pseudopregnancy, and anestrus) (15). 3α,5α-Tetrahydroprogesterone formation was lower in the pituitaries of constant estrus rats compared with the two subsequent stages, or to young cycling rats. These changes in metabolism may be important in regulating progesterone's effects during altered reproductive states, by varying amounts of inactive vs. active metabolites.

Characteristics of Pituitary and Hypothalamic Enzymes Catalyzing 5α- and 3α-Reduction of Progesterone

As shown in Figure 1, progesterone 5α-reduction is catalyzed by an irreversible, NADPH-dependent progesterone 5α-reductase. 5α-Dihydroprogesterone in turn is metabolized to 3α,5α-tetrahydroprogesterone by two distinct 5α-dihydroprogesterone 3α-HSORs: one that is cytosolic and prefers NADPH as a cofactor, and a second that is particulate and prefers NADH as a cofactor.

Progesterone 5α-Reductase

Progesterone 5α-reductases from both tissues have a dependence for NADPH and exhibit a K_m for progesterone (approximately 100 nM) consistent with reported plasma concentrations of progesterone (16,17). Their steroid specificity requires a conjugated Δ^4-3-ketone. Of the natural steroid hormones tested, only ovarian $\Delta^{4-3-\text{oxosteroids}}$ (20α-dihydroprogesterone and 17α-hydroxyprogesterone) competitively inhibit progesterone 5α-reduction within the range of their physiological plasma concentrations. Both 5α-reductases have ordered-sequential kinetic mechanisms (1,18,19) with NADPH binding preceding the binding of progesterone. Because intracellular concentrations of NADPH (approximately 10 to 400 µM) are greater than its K_m, these results suggest that the formation of 5α-reduced metabolites is a function of available progesterone (not NADPH) during times of changing progesterone levels. Hypothalamic 5α-reductase is inhibited by metal ions such as Zn^{2+} and Cu^{2+}, but enhanced by K^+ and Li^+. The pituitary enzyme is stimulated by specific phospholipids, which suggests that alterations in membrane composition may modulate pituitary progesterone 5α-reduction. Ovariectomy increases the activity of the pituitary enzyme 10- to 12-fold, whereas estrogen partially restores it (2,20).

3α-Hydroxysteroid Oxidoreductases

In the hypothalamus and pituitary, there are at least two different 5α-dihydroprogesterone 3α-HSOR activities that differ in subcellular location, cofactor requirement, pH and temperature optima and various kinetic parameters (21–23). In both tissues, an NADPH-linked activity is located in the cytosol, whereas an NADH-linked activity is found in the microsomal or cell membrane fractions of the pituitary or hypothalamus, respectively (21,22). Both 3α-HSORs (NADH- and NADPH-linked) catalyze the reversible oxidoreduction of 5α-dihydroprogesterone to 3α,5α-tetrahydroprogesterone. The NADH-linked 3α-HSORs apparently favor catalysis in the oxidative direction (i.e., 5α-dihydroprogesterone formation from 3α,5α-tetrahydroprogesterone), whereas the NADPH-linked 3α-HSORs apparently favor catalysis in the reductive direction (i.e., 3α,5α-tetrahydroprogesterone formation from 5α-dihydroprogesterone) (2). These 3α-HSORs could therefore differentially regulate levels of 5α-dihydroprogesterone and 3α,5α-tetrahydroprogesterone. Pituitary and hypothalamic NADPH-linked 3α-HSORs have K_ms of approximately 80 nM for 5α-dihydroprogesterone and 1 to 2 µM for 3α,5α-tetrahydroprogesterone. Pituitary NADH-linked 3α-HSOR has a K_m of 0.23 µM for

5α-dihydroprogesterone and 58 nM for 3α,5α-tetrahydroprogesterone. Corresponding hypothalamic values are 0.40 μM and 0.11 μM. Ovariectomy increases pituitary NADH-linked 3α-HSOR activity four- to fivefold, whereas estrogen partially restores it (20).

The pituitary cytosolic NADPH-linked 3α-HSOR has been purified and is a monomer of 36 kD which prefers C_{21} substrates (5α-dihydroprogesterone and 3α,5α-tetrahydroprogesterone) over the corresponding C_{19} substrates (5α-dihydrotestosterone and 3α,5α-tetrahydrotestosterone) (24,25). In contrast to liver cytosolic 3α-HSOR, the purified pituitary enzyme has no associated dihydrodiol dehydrogenase activity. Many 3-keto and 3α(β)-hydroxysteroids were tested as inhibitors or alternate substrates. Only deoxycorticosterone and ovarian progestins showed significant effects. None of the 3β- or 5β-isomers had any effect. The enzyme is potently inhibited by indomethacin (uncompetitive) and medroxyprogesterone (competitive).

Effects of Phenobarbital on Pituitary 3α-HSORs (NADH- and NADPH-linked)

Because 3α,5α-tetrahydroprogesterone and barbiturates affect the $GABA_A$ receptor (26–28), we tested the effects of phenobarbital on the two pituitary 3α-HSOR activities to see if barbiturates could influence the production of 3α,5α-tetrahydroprogesterone. Phenobarbital (1 to 10 mM) inhibited the *reductive* formation of 3α,5α-tetrahydroprogesterone from 5α-dihydroprogesterone (30% to 50%) by both (NADH- and NADPH-linked) enzymes. The *oxidative* conversion of 5α-dihydroprogesterone from 3α,5α-tetrahydroprogesterone was stimulated at 1 mM phenobarbital (60% to 100%) but inhibited (40% to 50%) at higher concentrations (10 to 25 mM). These results suggest that such concentrations of phenobarbital (within the range used pharmacologically) can influence 3α,5α-tetrahydroprogesterone formation and may be a means by which phenobarbital influences the $GABA_A$ receptor.

Can These Ubiquitous Steroid Metabolic Processing Steps Generate Specific Target Tissue Responses?

Unless the biological role of progesterone and its metabolites is greater than presently envisaged, these ubiquitous processing steps might appear to argue against the idea that in situ metabolic processing can be a specific target cellular mode of action. Many ubiquitous enzyme systems, such as adenyl cyclases, protein kinases and testosterone 5α-reductases, produce

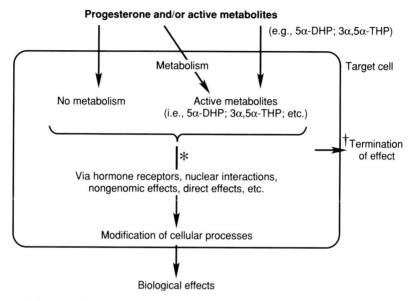

Figure 2. Suggested Model of Progesterone Action. Biological effects include effects on luteinizing hormone/follicle-stimulating hormone synthesis/release, lordosis behavior, anesthesia and modulation of GABA receptors. *Permissive or prior effects of other hormones. †Metabolism to inactive metabolites, degradation and exiting from cell.

tissue-specific effects because of *inter alia* tissue differences in the properties of these enzymes, levels of product(s) formed and differences in the responsive cellular processes in specific target tissues. In an analogous fashion, these widespread progesterone processing steps could be similarly envisaged to generate specificity. The several lines of evidence reviewed earlier support this idea and indicate (i) tissue differences in the quantitative formation of the various metabolites that could affect subsequent intracellular events in a concentration-dependent manner, and (ii) tissue differences in enzyme activity and in their catalytic and regulatory properties. In addition, specificity could be endowed by the differentiated function of a particular target tissue in which only certain progesterone-sensitive processes are expressed.

Conclusion

Substantial evidence indicates that the metabolic processing of progesterone and related neuroactive steroids by neural and neuroendocrine structures is an important component of the cellular mechanisms by which these steroids achieve their neural and neuroendocrine effects.

These results and those of other investigators support the proposed model of progesterone action (1,13) shown in Figure 2, whereby the diverse effects of progesterone may result from the action of progesterone itself, its metabolites, or from combinations. This processing of progesterone and other similar steroids appears to be a means by which the parent steroid is made into more active, less active, and/or inactive forms (1,2). These conversions may be important not only in reducing or ending progesterone's effects, but also in generating active metabolites to mediate effects. Some metabolites, by duplicating certain effects of progesterone, also may provide a means of prolonging some effects of progesterone while others are terminated.

References

1. Karavolas HJ, Hodges DR. Neuroendocrine metabolism of progesterone and related progestins. *Ciba Found Symp* 1990;153:22–55.
2. Karavolas HJ, Bertics PJ, Hodges DR, et al. Neuroendocrine metabolism of progesterone and related progestins. In: Celotti F, Naftolin F, Martini L, eds. *Metabolism of hormonal steroids in the neuroendocrine structures.* New York: Raven Press, 1984;149–170.
3. Karavolas HJ, Nuti KM. Progesterone metabolism by neuroendocrine tissues. In: Naftolin F, Ryan KJ, Davies TJ, eds. *Subcellular mechanisms in reproductive neuroendocrinology.* Amsterdam: Elsevier, 1976;305–326.
4. Rommerts F, Van der Molen HJ. Occurrence and localization of 5α-steroid reductase, 3α- and 17β-hydroxysteroid dehydrogenase in hypothalamus and other brain tissues of the male rat. *Biochem Biophys Acta* 1971;248:489–502.
5. Celotti F, Massa R, Martini L. Metabolism of steroids in the central nervous system. In: De Groot LJ, Cahill GF, Martini L, et al., eds. *Endocrinology,* vol 1. New York: Grune and Stratton, 1979;41–53.
6. Karavolas HJ, Hodges D, Normand N, et al. Conversion of 17α-hydroxyprogesterone to 5α, 3α and 20α-reduced metabolites by female rat anterior pituitary and hypothalamus. *Steroids* 1988;51:527–541.
7. Martini L. The 5α-reduction of testosterone in the neuroendocrine structures. Biochemical and physiological implications. *Endocr Rev* 1982;3:1–25.
8. Bäckström T, Gee KW, Lan N, et al. Steroids in relation to epilepsy and anesthesia. *Ciba Found Symp* 1990;153:225–239.
9. Hanukoglu I, Karavolas HJ, Goy RW. Progesterone metabolism in the pineal, brain stem, thalamus and corpus callosum of the female rat. *Brain Res* 1977;125:313–324.
10. Lloyd RV, Karavolas HJ. Uptake and conversion of progesterone and testosterone to 5α-reduced products by enriched gonadotropic and chromophobic rat anterior pituitary cell fractions. *Endocrinology* 1975;97:517–526.

11. Melcangi RC, Celotti F, Negri-Cesi P, et al. Testosterone 5α-reductase in discrete hypothalamic nuclear areas in the rat: effect of castration. *Steroids* 1985;45:347–356.

12. Bertics SJ, Bertics PJ, Clarke JL, et al. Distribution and ovarian control of progestin-metabolizing enzymes in various rat hypothalamic regions. *J Steroid Biochem* 1987;26:321–328.

13. Karavolas HJ, Hodges DR, O'Brien DJ. *In vivo* uptake and metabolism of [^{3}H] progesterone and [^{3}H] 5α-dihydroprogesterone by rat CNS and anterior pituitary: tissue concentration of progesterone itself or metabolites? *J Steroid Biochem* 1979;11:863–872.

14. Marrone BL, Karavolas HJ. Progesterone metabolism by the hypothalamus, pituitary and uterus of the rat during pregnancy. *Endocrinology* 1981;109:41–45.

15. Marrone BL, Karavolas HJ. Progesterone metabolism by the hypothalamus, pituitary and uterus of the aged rat. *Endocrinology* 1982;111:162–167.

16. Bertics PJ, Karavolas HJ. Partial characterization of the microsomal and solubilized hypothalamic progesterone 5α-reductase. *J Steroid Biochem* 1984;21:305–314.

17. Bertics PJ, Karavolas HJ. Pituitary progesterone 5α-reductase: solubilization and partial characterization. *J Steroid Biochem* 1985;22:795–802.

18. Campbell JS, Bertics PJ, Karavolas HJ. The kinetic mechanism of the anterior pituitary progesterone 5α-reductase. *J Steroid Biochem* 1986;24:801–806.

19. Campbell JS, Karavolas HJ. The kinetic mechanism of the hypothalamic progesterone 5α-reductase. *J Steroid Biochem* 1989;32:283–289.

20. Krause JE, Bertics PJ, Karavolas HJ. Ovarian regulation of hypothalamic and pituitary progestin-metabolizing enzyme activities. *Endocrinology* 1981;108:1–7.

21. Krause JE, Karavolas HJ. Subcellular location of hypothalamic progesterone metabolizing enzymes and evidence for distinct NADH and NADPH-linked 3α-hydroxysteroid oxidoreductase activities. *J Steroid Biochem* 1980;13:271–280.

22. Krause JE, Karavolas HJ. Pituitary 5α-dihydroprogesterone 3α-hydroxysteroid oxidoreductase: subcellular location and properties of NADH- and NADPH-linked activities. *J Biol Chem* 1980;255:11807–11814.

23. Krause JE, Karavolas HJ. Properties of the hypothalamic 5α-dihydroprogesterone NADH- and NADPH-linked 3α-hydroxysteroid oxidoreductase activities. *J Steroid Biochem* 1980;14:63–69.

24. Campbell JS, Karavolas HJ. Purification of the NADPH: 5α-dihydroprogesterone 3α-hydroxysteroid oxidoreductase from female rat pituitary cytosol. *J Steroid Biochem Mol Biol* 1990;37:215–222.

25. Campbell JS, Karavolas HJ. Characterization of the purified pituitary cytosolic NADPH: 5α-dihydroprogesterone 3α-hydroxysteroid oxidoreductase. *J Steroid Biochem Mol Biol* 1990;37:535–543.

26. Majewska MD, Harrison NL, Schwartz RD, et al. Steroid metabolites are barbiturate-like modulators of the GABA receptor. *Science* 1986;232:1004–1007.

27. Gee KW. Steroid modulation of the GABA/benzodiazepine receptor-linked chloride ionophore. *Mol Neurobiol* 1988;2:291–317.

28. Lambert JJ, Peters JA, Sturgess NC, et al. Steroid modulation of the GABA$_A$ receptor complex: electrophysiological studies. *Ciba Found Symp* 1990;153:56–82.

Neurosteroids:
Biosynthesis and Metabolism in Cultured Rodent Glia and Neurons

P. Robel, M.D., I. Jung-Testas, Ph.D., Z.Y. Hu, Ph.D., Y. Akwa,
N. Sananes, Ph.D., K. Kabbadj, B. Eychenne, M.J. Sancho, K.I. Kang,
D. Zucman, M.D., R. Morfin, Ph.D., and E.E. Baulieu, M.D., Ph.D.

INSERM U33, Lab. Hormones, F-94275 Bicêtre Cedex, France

The characterization of pregnenolone (P), dehydroepiandrosterone (D), their sulfate esters (S) and their fatty acid esters (lipoidal derivatives, L) in the rat brain, and the observation of their large cerebral accumulation in other mammalian species (mouse, pig, guinea pig, monkey and human) led us to reconsider steroid-brain interrelationships. We observed that, besides the large difference between brain and blood concentrations of D and DS, the cerebral concentrations were apparently independent of adrenal and gonadal sources. Therefore, we started to measure P, the immediate biochemical precursor of D in steroidogenic cells of peripheral glands, and the results confirmed those obtained with D. Because no evidence was obtained either for extraglandular sources or for release from known derivatives stored in the brain, the hypothesis of de novo synthesis of P and D was considered. However, all attempts to demonstrate the side-chain cleavage of cholesterol by brain slices, total homogenates or mitochondrial preparations were unsuccessful.

Thus, we decided to use immunohistochemical means to look for the presence of specific enzymes involved in cholesterol side-chain cleavage. Cytochrome P-450$_{scc}$ (scc, side-chain cleavage) is found in mitochondria of all steroidogenic endocrine cells as part of a three-enzyme hydroxylase system with adrenodoxin reductase and adrenodoxin. P-450$_{scc}$ was purified from bovine adrenal mitochondria, and specific antisera were generated. We used the corresponding IgGs (kindly provided by M. Waterman) to set up an immunohistochemical technique for the detection of cyto-chrome P-450$_{scc}$ in rat tissues. Specific immune staining was detected in the white matter throughout the brain. Because the myelin of the white matter is made by a particular type of glial cells, the oligodendrocytes, we isolated oligodendrocyte mitochondria, incubated them with [^{3}H]cho-lesterol, and obtained [^{3}H]P and its reduced derivative [^{3}H]-20-OH-P ([^{3}H]pregn-5-en-3β,20α diol).

Pregnenolone Formation from Sterol Precursors

Newborn rat glial cell cultures were incubated in the presence of [^{3}H]mevalonolactone ([^{3}H]MVA). The endogenous supply of mevalonate was restricted by the use of mevinolin (20 μM), a specific inhibitor of 3β-hydroxy 3β-methyl glutaryl CoA reductase. Trilostane, a specific inhibitor of Δ5–3β-hydroxysteroid dehydrogenase-isomerase (3β-HSD), also was added to prevent, in part, further metabolism of P.

In preliminary experiments, ≥3-week-old cultures were able to convert [^{3}H]MVA to tritiated cholesterol, P and 20-OH-P. When dibutyryl (db) cAMP was added to the culture medium, the conversion of [^{3}H]MVA to combined [^{3}H]P and [^{3}H]-20-OH-P was almost twice as large as in control cultures. Therefore, most subsequent incubations contained 0.2 mM db cAMP.

Cells dissociated from the cerebral hemispheres of newborn rats were maintained in long-term culture with progressive differentiation of oligo-dendrocytes and astrocytes. Both cell types were characterized by indirect immunofluorescence with monoclonal antibodies to galactocerebroside (Gal C) and to glial fibrillary acidic protein, respectively. To follow oligo-dendrocyte differentiation, we measured the activity of the enzyme 2'-3'-cyclic nucleotide 3'-phosphodiesterase (CNPase). After day 10 in our culture conditions, CNPase activity and the biosynthesis of P increased in parallel, reaching their highest levels at day 21. This result suggested that the onset of steroidogenic activity was related to oligodendroglial differentiation. Indeed, after 3 weeks in culture, approximately 60% of the cells were mature oligodendrocytes. They showed highly branched processes specific of differentiated cells, their number had increased, they covered the layer of polygonal astrocytes, and their cytoplasm was specifically and intensely immunostained with anti–P-450$_{scc}$ IgGs. Double labeling experiments were performed. As a rule, cells immunostained with the antibody to Gal C also reacted with anti–P-450$_{scc}$ IgGs. Four- to 10-week-old cultures still expressed Gal C and CNPase at about the same level as 3-week-old cultures.

Astrocytes were only slightly immunoreactive with anti–P-450$_{scc}$ IgGs, and were unlikely to contribute significantly to the production of steroids. However, astrocytes may exert a positive influence on the differentiation and even on the steroidogenic activity of oligodendrocytes.

Aminoglutethimide (AG) is a potent inhibitor of P-450$_{scc}$. When adrenal cells are incubated with AG, cholesterol accumulates in mitochondria and is available for side-chain cleavage when the inhibitor is removed. We obtained similar results with newborn rat glial cells after 3 weeks of culture. During the incubation of primary cultures with [^{3}H]MVA for 48 hr in the presence of AG, glial cells accumulated [^{3}H]cholesterol. The culture medium was removed and the cells were further incubated for 16 hr in the presence of db cAMP and trilostane, but with neither mevinolin nor [^{3}H]MVA. After the release of AG blockade, [^{3}H]-20-OH-P was found in the culture medium, whereas [^{3}H]cholesterol was formed in the cells and represented approximately 10% of the radioactivity in cell extracts. Addition of dexamethasone to the culture medium for 64 hr resulted in a 30% increased rate of [^{3}H]-20-OH-P synthesis, contrasting with a large inhibition of intracellular [^{3}H]cholesterol. Thus, the 20-OH-P/cholesterol ratio was increased twofold by dexamethasone. This effect of dexamethasone may be related to its influence on oligodendroglial differentiation and on the early phase of myelination, and/or to enhanced cAMP production and steroid synthesis.

Pregnenolone Metabolism by Brain Cell Types

Preliminary experiments in which rat brain minces had been incubated with [^{3}H]P (0.6 μM) yielded [^{3}H]progesterone ([^{3}H]PRO) and [^{3}H]PL. The conversion to [^{3}H]PRO was in the 1% range per 100 mg tissue per 3 hr in the hypothalamus, amygdala, olfactory bulb and other regions of the brain except the cerebellum and frontal cortex, where virtually no metabolism was observed. Then, we attempted to define the cell types that contained the 3β-HSD responsible for the conversion of P to PRO. For that purpose, we incubated primary glial cell cultures (containing a mixed population of astrocytes and oligodendrocytes), with [^{3}H]P in concentration (65 pmol/ml) corresponding to the average amount of P found in the adult rat brain, for 24 hr in the presence of db cAMP but without trilostane. After incubation, extracts from cells and media were analyzed by thin-layer chromatography (TLC). Among the radioactive metabolites observed, we found a radioactive compound with the R$_f$ of PRO, representing about 3% of the total radioactivity. [^{3}H]PRO was further characterized by reverse-phase high-performance liquid chromatography (HPLC) and by crystallization after reverse isotopic dilution.

Other radioactive metabolites were found, migrating with the respective R_f of 5α-pregnane-3,20-dione (pregnanedione) and of 3α-hydroxy-5α-pregnane-20-dione (3α-pregnanolone), respectively. They were identified by HPLC and by crystallization after reverse isotopic dilution. Other polar and nonpolar metabolites also were found. The nonpolar fraction was analyzed after saponification: about two-thirds of its radioactivity migrated as authentic P on TLC. The polar metabolites contained 20-OH-P and an abundant compound, which is quite polar, later tentatively identified as 7α-OH-P.

Indeed, with NADPH as a cofactor, brain microsomes converted P to a prominent polar metabolite with chromatographic properties similar to those of the metabolite observed in glial cell cultures. Formation of this compound was inhibited by carbon monoxide, indicating the involvement of cytochrome P-450. Microsomes were incubated with double-labeled ^{14}C- and [^{2}H]P. The doubly labeled polar metabolite was analyzed by gas chromatography–mass spectrometry, with a retention time and fragmentation pattern identical to that of authentic reference compound; the percent deuterium in excess of natural abundance was in accordance with the value in double-labeled substrate. Therefore, 7α-OH-P was considered as rigorously identified.

P metabolism by astroglial cells also has been investigated. Cells were mechanically dissociated from the cerebral cortex or striatum of 17-day-old rat embryos. Selective culture conditions were used, which allowed the growth of astroglial cells (mainly type 1 astrocytes), and the culture contained no neurons, no fibroblasts, no oligodendrocytes, and few microglia. After 3 weeks of culture, the cells were incubated with 100 nM [^{3}H]P for 24 hr, with or without 4-MAPC [4-methyl-3-oxo-4-aza-5α-pregnane-20(s) carboxylate, MSD L-642, 022–01V03], a 5α-reductase inhibitor, and trilostane, a 3β-HSD inhibitor. The steroids were extracted and separated by TLC. Further characterization of radioactive PRO, pregnanedione, 3α-pregnanolone and 20-OH-P was performed by reverse-phase HPLC, followed by crystallization after reverse isotopic dilution.

Astroglial cells from the cerebral cortex and from the striatum metabolized [^{3}H]P to [^{3}H]PRO, [^{3}H]pregnanedione and [^{3}H]-3α-pregnanolone. Cells from the cerebral cortex tended to be more active than those from the striatum. The amounts of PRO and its metabolites formed were about fourfold smaller than in newborn rat glial cell cultures. 4-MAPC completely suppressed pregnanedione and 3α-pregnanolone.

Dissociated brain cells from 17-day-old mouse embryos also were cultured in media that only allow the growth of neurons (MEM/FR medium supplemented with insulin, transferrin, PRO, putrescine and selenium). On the fifth day of culture, the cells were incubated with ^{14}C-P for 24 hr. The metabolites were separated by two-dimensional TLC (benzene/methanol 19:1 followed by cyclohexane/ethyl acetate 4/6) and submitted to autoradiography. The extracts of cells and media contained no radioactive compound with the migration of PRO or its 5α-reduced metabolites. The only compound identified was 20-OH-P, which represented 3.2% of the incubated ^{14}C-P, almost exclusively in the medium. The major metabolite formed was quite polar and was not identified. Neuron cultures incubated with ^{14}C-PRO yielded pregnane-dione and a mixture of 3β-hydroxy-5α-pregnane-20-one (pregnanolone) and 3α-pregnanolone.

Dehydroepiandrosterone Metabolism

We have devoted major efforts to the elucidation of D formation in the brain, because indirect evidence indicated that the accumulation of D in the mammalian brain appeared independent of peripheral steroidogenic glands.

However, incubations of [^{3}H]P with brain slices, homogenates and microsomes, or with primary cultures of mixed glial cells, or with astrocytes and neurons of rat or mouse embryos, never produced a radioactive metabolite with the chromatographic behavior of [^{3}H]D. Also, all attempts were unsuccessful to demonstrate the P-450$_{17\alpha}$ antigen immunohistochemically in the rat brain with antibodies to the enzyme purified from pig testis (kindly donated by Ian Mason), and in the guinea pig brain with specific antibodies to the enzyme from the guinea pig adrenal (kindly donated by S. Takemori).

Newborn rat glial cells or fetal astroglial cells in culture metabolized D into a prominent polar metabolite with the chromatographic properties of 7α-OH-D. A similar compound was observed after incubation of brain microsomes in the presence of either double-labeled [14]C- and [^{2}H]D, or [^{3}H]D. The metabolite was formally identified as such, or after reduction to androst-5-ene-3β, 7α, 17β triol, by gas-liquid chromatography–mass spectrometry, using a similar approach to the one described for the identification of 7α-OH-P, and also by recrystallization to constant specific activity after isotopic dilution with authentic reference compound.

When glial cell cultures were bubbled with carbon monoxide then incubated with ^{14}C-D, the conversion to the polar metabolite tentatively identified as 7α-OH-D was blocked. Consequently, alternative metabolic pathways could be observed, namely formation of the D-reduced metabolite androst-5-ene-3β, 17β diol, which has weak estrogenic potency, and of androstenedione.

Conjugation of Neurosteroids

Both P and D are found in part as ester sulfates in the brain, the concentration of DS exceeding that of D. No special efforts have been made to detect the conversion of [³H]P or [³H]D to their sulfate esters by incubation of brain slices and homogenates, or of primary glial cell cultures.

The major conjugation forms of P and D in the brain are their fatty acid esters (PL and DL). The acyltransferase responsible for their formation is enriched in the microsomal fraction and uses endogenous fatty acids for the esterification of steroids. Formation of nonpolar metabolites that release P or D after saponification has been observed after incubation of the corresponding ¹⁴C-labeled substrate with all types of brain cells. However, because culture media containing serum or serum substitutes also can metabolize neurosteroids to saponifiable nonpolar derivatives, the exact cellular localization of steroid acyltransferase(s) awaits further investigation.

Steroid-Metabolizing Enzymes in Brain Cell Types

The cholesterol-desmolase complex, which associates cytochrome P-450$_{scc}$, ferredoxin, and ferredoxin reductase, appears localized almost exclusively in oligodendrocytes (Table 1). The P-450$_{17\alpha}$ enzyme has not yet been found in the brain. P-450$_{7\alpha}$ activity is prominent, is definitely localized in all types of glial cells, and also is likely present in neurons. Low 3β-HSD activity is present in glial cells, whereas neurons seem inactive. Conversely, the 5α-reductase and 3α-hydroxysteroid oxidoreductase (3α-HOR) activities are present in both glial cells and neurons, whereas the 3β-HOR activity predominates in astroglial cells and in neurons. Therefore, the neurons seem to lack two major enzymes in the pathway from cholesterol to pregnanolones, P-450$_{scc}$ and 3β-HSD, and need the cooperation of glial cells for these bioconversions.

Involvement of Metabolism in Neurosteroid Mechanism(s) of Action

The 3β-hydroxy-Δ5-steroids accumulated in the brain are potential precursors of corresponding Δ4–3 keto-steroid "classical" hormones. We

Table 1. Enzymes of steroid metabolism in brain cells

Enzyme	Substrate	Newborn Mixed glial	Fetus Astroglial	Neurons
P-450$_{scc}$	P	+	nd	nd
P-450$_{17\alpha}$	P PRO	nd	nd	nd
20α-HOR	P PRO	+	+	+
P-450$_{7\alpha}$	P D	+	+	(+)
3β-HSD	P D	+	+	nd
5α-R	P D	+	+	+
3ζ-HOR	P-dione	3α	3β > 3α	3β >> 3α

P-450: cytochrome P-450. 20α-HOR: 20α-hydroxysteroid oxidoreductase. 3β-HSD: Δ5–3β-hydroxysteroid dehydrogenase-isomerase. 5α-R: 5α-reductase. 3ζ-HOR: 3α- or 3β-hydroxysteroid oxidoreductase. P: pregnenolone. PRO: progesterone. D: dehydroepiandrosterone. P-dione: 5α-pregnane-3,20-dione. (+): Tentatively identified. nd: Not detected.

have shown the transformation of P into PRO. Locally formed PRO, if it has a physiological role, may act paracrinally or autocrinally. Indeed, glial cells contain a PRO receptor, inducible by estrogens. The PRO receptor already has been detected in the hypothalamus, in the cortex and in meningiomas. The concentration of PRO in the brain of young adult male rats is not negligible (about 1 to 2 ng/g of tissue). However, the contribution of brain synthesis to it is yet unknown. The transformation of D into androstenedione occurs in the same brain areas as that of P into PRO, but no further conversion into testosterone has been detected so far.

P and D do not bind to any known *intracellular receptor*. Low-affinity P binding proteins have been described in other tissues of the rat and the guinea pig. The concentration of P in the brain is quite compatible with binding to such protein(s). A heat-stable P binding protein has been found in brain cytosol (D. Zucman, unpublished data). The K_d for P is approximately 80 nM. The relative binding affinities are as follows: P (100%), 3β-hydroxy-5α-pregnane-20-one (68%), pregn-5-ene-3β,20α-diol (5%), PRO (42%), D (20%), pregnanedione (10%). Neither PS nor DS, corticosterone, T, and E_2 bind. The relevance of P binding protein to the mechanism of accumulation of P and D in the brain is under current investigation.

The γ-aminobutyric acid (GABA)$_A$ receptor is an oligomeric protein complex which, when activated by agonists, produces an increase in membrane conductance to Cl^- ions, resulting in reduced neuronal excitability. 3α-Pregnanolone both mimics and enhances the effects of GABA. Our results indicate that PRO might be converted to the inhibitory steroid metabolites by target neurons. Conversely, PS, at micromolar concentrations, interacts with the GABA$_A$ receptor complex as a picrotoxin-like antagonist. Under optimal conditions, [^{3}H]DS was bound to brain synaptosomal membranes, likewise at the level of the GABA$_A$ receptor with K_d 1.3 μM and B_{max} 308 pmol/mg protein. The binding of [^{3}H]DS was competed by several steroid sulfates, in order of decreasing relative binding (DS taken as 100%): 3α-pregnanolone S (468) > epiandrosterone S (125) > DS (100) > 3β-pregnanolone S (95) > androstenediol 3-S (77) > PS (43) > androsterone S (26) > 5β-androsterone S (12). Neither the ester sulfates of cholesterol and corticosterone nor unconjugated 3α-pregnanolone and D competed for the binding of [^{3}H]DS.

Therefore, PS and 3α-pregnanolone have opposite effects on GABA$_A$ receptors and seem to interact with distinct binding sites on the receptor complex; thus, P metabolites in the brain as well as steroids of extraencephalic sources may be involved physiologically in GABA$_A$ receptor function.

In conclusion, the functional significance of neurosteroids needs further investigation, although the data at hand suggest autocrine and/or paracrine roles.

Regulation of Steroid Synthesis in the Adrenals by Mitochondrial Benzodiazepine Receptors

*Karl E. Krueger, Ph.D., Michael E. Whalin, Ph.D., and *Vassilios Papadopoulos, Ph.D.*

*Fidia-Georgetown Institute for the Neurosciences, *Department of Anatomy and Cell Biology, Georgetown University School of Medicine, Washington, D.C. 20007*

The molecular events underlying steroid hormone biosynthesis and its regulation have been the subject of intensive investigations (1). The acute stimulation of steroidogenesis is principally regulated at the first step in this biosynthetic pathway, which is catalyzed by cytochrome $P\text{-}450_{scc}$ (scc, side-chain cleavage), where cholesterol is converted to pregnenolone, the parent of all steroids. The $P\text{-}450_{scc}$ enzyme catalyzing this side-chain cleavage of cholesterol is localized on inner mitochondrial membranes. Detailed studies demonstrated that the enzymatic kinetics of $P\text{-}450_{scc}$ are not rate-determining in steroid biosynthesis but, rather, the limiting factor is the rate of transport of the substrate cholesterol from intracellular sites to $P\text{-}450_{scc}$ on inner mitochondrial membranes. The pituitary hormones adrenocorticotropin (ACTH) and gonadotropin act at their endocrine target tissues by binding to cell surface receptors coupled with the stimulation of adenylate cyclase, thereby triggering a complex series of intracellular events leading to increased transport of cholesterol to $P\text{-}450_{scc}$.

Further studies have shown that cycloheximide completely blocks the stimulation by pituitary tropic hormones. This inhibition occurs at a stage involving the mitochondrion, specifically, at the regulatory step of cholesterol transfer to the inner mitochondrial membrane (2). Although intramitochondrial cholesterol transport is central to understanding the regulation of steroidogenesis, the molecular components functioning in this process have proven difficult to identify.

Previous studies revealed a salient relationship of peripheral-type benzodiazepine recognition sites with steroidogenic tissues. This specific class of binding sites includes a mitochondrial site that is distinct from a site on γ-aminobutyric acid (GABA) receptors, although its function was not known until recently. In an attempt to elucidate a function for this other class of recognition sites for benzodiazepines, we considered two important points. First, these sites are present in many tissues but are extremely abundant in steroidogenic cells. Second, the sites are found primarily on outer mitochondrial membranes, and therefore are referred to herein as mitochondrial benzodiazepine receptors (MBRs). Because steroidogenesis is regulated at the level of the mitochondrion, this information prompted us to investigate whether MBRs play a role in this biosynthetic pathway.

To investigate the possibility that MBRs function in steroid biosynthesis, we used the mouse adrenocortical tumor Y-1 cell line (3). Y-1 cells exhibited a high density of MBRs (approximately 50 pmol/mg cellular protein), which is characteristic of steroidogenic tissues. A series of 10 ligands, differing by more than 4 orders of magnitude in their affinities for MBRs, were tested for their effects on 20α-hydroxyprogesterone secretion, the major steroid product of Y-1 cells. All ligands with submicromolar affinities for MBRs stimulated steroidogenesis, with the highest-affinity ligands alpidem, PK-11195, (−)PK-14067, and Ro5–4864 showing the greatest efficacy (twofold over basal levels). In contrast, the benzodiazepines clonazepam and flumazenil, which have the greatest selectivity for $GABA_A$ receptors, did not stimulate steroidogenesis. A highly significant correlation ($r = 0.98$) was observed between the potencies of this series of ligands to stimulate steroidogenesis compared with their affinities for MBRs. This finding suggests that the effects of the drugs were in fact mediated via MBRs. Similar observations were made in bovine and rat adrenocortical cell preparations (3), purified rat Leydig cells, and the mouse Leydig tumor MA-10 cell line (4).

Further studies were conducted to elucidate the mechanism by which MBRs mediate the stimulation in steroidogenesis. In isolated mitochondrial fractions, PK-11195 and Ro5–4864 induced a twofold stimulation of pregnenolone synthesis, whereas clonazepam was ineffective. If, however, mitoplasts prepared by removing the outer mitochondrial membranes were used, the MBR ligands failed to stimulate pregnenolone synthesis, consistent with the proposed location of MBRs. Furthermore, the MBR ligands had no effect on steroid synthesis when cells or mitochondrial fractions were incubated with 22(R)-hydroxycholesterol. This observation demonstrates that the ligands do not directly stimulate P-450$_{scc}$.

The stimulation of steroid secretion by ACTH in Y-1 cells is completely inhibited by cycloheximide, whereas the stimulation by PK-11195 is unaffected by this protein synthesis inhibitor. When Y-1 cells are pretreated with ACTH and cycloheximide simultaneously, to promote cholesterol transport to mitochondria, the efficacy of PK-11195 is markedly enhanced. This finding suggests that MBRs participate in the steroidogenic pathway downstream of the step blocked by cycloheximide (5).

To examine whether MBRs mediate intramitochondrial cholesterol transport, mitochondria were incubated in the presence or absence of 1 μM PK-11195 with aminoglutethimide, an inhibitor of P-450$_{scc}$. Subsequent subfractionation of outer and inner mitochondrial membrane fractions showed that PK-11195 increased the level of cholesterol associated with the inner membranes, at the expense of the outer membrane fractions. Hence, these findings provide direct evidence that MBRs play a role in intramitochondrial cholesterol transport, the rate-determining step of steroid biosynthesis.

In light of these findings, it is important to consider whether MBRs participate in the physiological stimulation of steroidogenesis, as induced by pituitary tropic hormones. When Y-1 cells, in the presence of maximal doses of ACTH, are treated with MBR ligands of higher affinity, such as PK-11195 or Ro5–4864, or with drugs of lower affinity, including diazepam and zolpidem, no effect on steroidogenesis is observed. In contrast, different results are obtained with flunitrazepam (6). This benzodiazepine acts as a partial agonist in control Y-1 cells, but in cells treated simultaneously with ACTH, flunitrazepam inhibits the hormone stimulation of steroidogenesis by 60%. The IC$_{50}$ for this effect is about 500 nM, in close agreement with the affinity of flunitrazepam for MBRs in Y-1 cells. The antagonistic action of flunitrazepam consisted of a reduction of the efficacy but not the potency of ACTH. Similarly, flunitrazepam inhibited steroidogenesis elicited by dibutyryl-cAMP. This finding suggests that flunitrazepam blocks the activation of steroid biosynthesis at a step subsequent to the elevation of intracellular cAMP levels.

Supporting evidence that the inhibition by flunitrazepam was mediated specifically by binding to MBRs is implied by Scatchard analysis, where only one class of specific binding sites for flunitrazepam is detected. Specific binding of flunitrazepam is completely displaceable by a series of MBR ligands showing a rank order characteristic of MBR specificity. Furthermore, these competing ligands prevent the antagonism by flunitrazepam with the same order of potency (r = 0.99), which is consistent with previous observations that the competing ligands have no effect on ACTH-stimulated steroid synthesis. These findings unequivocally demonstrate that the inhibition of tropic hormone–induced steroidogenesis by flunitrazepam is due to its specific interaction with MBRs. This observation further implies that MBRs are coupled to the physiological activation of steroidogenesis by pituitary tropic hormones.

Some important questions regarding the antagonism by flunitrazepam, however, remain unanswered. For example, why flunitrazepam does not completely inhibit the tropic hormone stimulation of steroidogenesis is unknown. A simple explanation may be that at least two mechanisms are operative in the rate-limiting step of steroidogenesis—an MBR-dependent and an MBR-independent mechanism. Another possibility may provide insight into the molecular mechanisms underlying the regulation of MBR function in steroidogenesis. Because flunitrazepam, by itself, acts as a partial agonist in steroidogenesis, this benzodiazepine apparently does not block the function of MBRs. Instead, flunitrazepam may interfere, at least partially, with the ability of the tropic hormone-induced response to activate MBRs in this pathway. Nevertheless, the reasons why flunitrazepam, but not other MBR partial agonists antagonize the tropic hormone action are still unknown.

With particular relevance to the role of MBRs in the actions triggered by tropic hormones, recent studies examining the intracellular mechanisms regulating steroid synthesis following tropic hormone activation suggest that the polypeptide diazepam binding inhibitor (DBI) can stimulate pregnenolone synthesis in adrenocortical mitochondrial fractions (7). Although DBI was first discovered and purified from the rat brain based on its ability to displace diazepam from rat brain membranes and to inhibit GABA-activated chloride channel gating allosterically, it also was found to displace ligands from MBRs (8). We therefore examined whether different MBR ligands affected the DBI stimulation of pregnenolone synthesis (9). In Y-1 cell mitochondrial preparations, DBI potently stimulated pregnenolone formation (EC_{50} approximately 80 nM). The stimulation by PK-11195 was found to be nonadditive with that of DBI. Moreover, flunitrazepam inhibited by about 70% the stimulation by DBI, suggesting that DBI mediates its action via an interaction with MBRs. These observations parallel those found previously with the action of ACTH on intact Y-1 cells. It might be inferred from this conspicuous correlation that tropic hormone stimulation of steroidogenesis involves a mechanism that regulates the interaction of DBI or its processing products, with MBRs in controlling the rate of this biosynthetic pathway.

In addition to the role of DBI, the possibility also has been investigated that the intracellular actions by tropic hormones involve a phosphorylation mechanism. In rat adrenocortical mitochondrial preparations, the catalytic subunit of protein kinase A promotes the phosphorylation of several major protein species, including an 18-kD protein that co-migrates with the MBR protein photolabeled with [^{3}H]PK-14105. In contrast, protein kinase C, calcium-calmodulin-dependent protein kinase II, and cGMP-dependent protein kinase do not affect phosphorylation of this protein. These findings imply that a cAMP-dependent phosphorylation mechanism may participate in the regulation of MBR function. Further studies will need to establish whether flunitrazepam alters the ability of protein kinase A to promote phosphorylation of the 18-kD protein. Moreover, the state of phosphorylation may be important in regulating the steroidogenic efficacy mediated by MBRs and DBI. Thus, these findings may provide important clues concerning the molecular mechanisms underlying the regulation of steroidogenesis.

References

1. Hall PF. Cellular organization for steroidogenesis. *Int Rev Cytol* 1984;86:53–95.
2. Privalle CT, Crivello JF, Jefcoate CR. Regulation of intramitochondrial cholesterol transfer to side-chain cleavage cytochrome P-450 in rat adrenal gland. *Proc Natl Acad Sci USA* 1983;80:702–706.
3. Mukhin AG, Papadopoulos V, Costa E, et al. Mitochondrial benzodiazepine receptors regulate steroid biosynthesis. *Proc Natl Acad Sci USA* 1989;86:9813–9816.
4. Papadopoulos V, Mukhin AG, Costa E, et al. The peripheral-type benzodiazepine receptor is functionally linked to Leydig cell steroidogenesis. *J Biol Chem* 1990;265:3772–3779.
5. Krueger KE, Papadopoulos V. Peripheral-type benzodiazepine receptors mediate translocation of cholesterol from outer to inner mitochondrial membranes in adrenocortical cells. *J Biol Chem* 1990;265:15015–15022.
6. Papadopoulos V, Nowzari FB, Krueger KE. Hormone-stimulated steroidogenesis is coupled to mitochondrial benzodiazepine receptors. *J Biol Chem* 1991;266:3682–3687.
7. Besman MJ, Yanagibashi K, Lee TD, et al. Identification of des-(Gly-Ile)-endozepine as an effector of corticotropin-dependent adrenal steroidogenesis: stimulation of cholesterol delivery is mediated by the peripheral benzodiazepine receptor. *Proc Natl Acad Sci USA* 1989;86:4897–4901.

8. Guidotti A, Berkovich A, Ferrarese C, et al. Neuronal-glial differential processing of DBI to yield ligands to central and peripheral benzodiazepine recognition sites. In: Sauvant JP, Langer SZ, Morselli PL, eds. *L.E.R.S. monograph series, imidazopyridines in sleep disorders,* vol 6. New York: Raven Press, 1988;25–38.

9. Papadopoulos V, Berkovich A, Krueger KE, et al. Diazepam binding inhibitor (DBI) and its processing products stimulate mitochondrial steroid biosynthesis via an interaction with mitochondrial benzodiazepine receptors. *Endocrinology* 1991;129:1481–1488.

Regulation of the Side-Chain Cleavage of Cholesterol by Endozepine (Benzodiazepine Binding Inhibitor, DBI)

A. Shane Brown, Peter F. Hall, M.D., Ph.D., and Kazu Yanagibashi, Ph.D.

Department of Endocrinology, Prince of Wales Hospital, Randwick, 2031 New South Wales, Australia; and Fuji Central Laboratory, Mochida Pharmaceutical Company, Shizuoka-ken 412, Japan

Endozepine, also known as benzodiazepine binding inhibitor (DBI), is known to stimulate steroidogenesis in adrenocortical and gonadal cells (1,2). The slow step in the synthesis of steroids is believed to involve the transport of the substrate cholesterol from storage depots in the cytoplasm to the inner mitochondrial membrane, where the pathway begins with the conversion of cholesterol to pregnenolone (3). This pregnenolone must leave the mitochondrion to undergo enzymatic transformation to the final secreted steroid hormone (such as cortisol or testosterone) (3). Transport of cholesterol occurs in several steps. Transport to the outer mitochondrial membrane requires actin and other components of the cytoskeleton (3), and transport from the outer to the inner membrane requires newly synthesized protein, not the cytoskeleton (4,5). Moreover, these steps are accelerated by the trophic hormones adrenocorticotropic hormone (ACTH) and luteinizing hormone (LH), and their second messenger cyclic AMP (3).

In search of proteins that might promote the transport of cholesterol at one or more steps in the pathway described in the text above, we reasoned that such proteins should increase the conversion of cholesterol to pregnenolone by isolated mitochondria from one of the steroidogenic cells. This process could occur because the supply of substrate appears to limit the rate of this conversion. We decided to use fasciculata cells from bovine adrenal cortex because large amounts of tissue appeared necessary for the isolation of a protein we suspected to be present in small amounts. We therefore established an assay based on incubation of fresh bovine adrenocortical mitochondria with cholesterol, and with and without subcellular fractions obtained during purification. The end point of the assay was based on measurement of pregnenolone.

Using this assay we isolated from supernate of bovine adrenal cortex a protein of approximately 9,000 MW, which increases the conversion of cholesterol to pregnenolone by bovine adrenocortical mitochondria (6). In addition, the protein promotes transport of cholesterol from outer to inner mitochondrial membranes when the two membranes are coincubated in the presence of endozepine and then separated by centrifugation. During these studies we isolated sufficient amounts of the protein (originally called 8.2K because of its size) to subject samples to microdetermination of amino acid sequence. We were surprised to learn that the protein in question was endozepine, or DBI (7).

The enzyme responsible for the conversion of cholesterol to pregnenolone is cytochrome $P\text{-}450_{scc}$ (scc, side-chain cleavage) located in the inner leaflet of the inner mitochondrial membrane (8). When any cytochrome P-450 binds its substrate, the heme iron becomes displaced from the plane of the pyrrole ring system and rearrangement of d orbital electrons causes loss of the sixth bond of the iron, which then becomes pentavalent. This rearrangement of the heme iron results from the conformational change associated with binding of the substrate and leads to a shift of the Soret peak from 420 nm or thereabout, to approximately 390 nm (8). This so-called type I spectral shift can be conveniently measured by difference spectroscopy, accurately, rapidly and without destroying the enzyme. Using this method, endozepine was found to cause increased binding of cholesterol to homogeneous cytochrome $P\text{-}450_{scc}$ so that a given concentration of cholesterol produces a greater spectral shift ($A_{390-420}$) in the presence of endozepine than in its absence. In other words, endozepine increases the proportion of molecules of P-450 that bind cholesterol. Under the conditions used, the rate of substrate binding did not change—only the final amount of binding is altered by endozepine.

For the most part, enzymes appear to bind substrates rapidly, but in the case of $P\text{-}450_{scc}$ there appears to be some delay in this process. Cholesterol is, of course, a structural component of membranes and its recruitment to the bound form may involve time-dependent changes. One such change may be the movement of cholesterol from the outer to the inner leaflet of the inner mitochondrial membrane (9). However, as far as endozepine is concerned, it is the affinity of the enzyme for its substrate that is altered by the peptide. Because such a change in enzyme-substrate affinity was observed with the homogeneous enzyme in a membrane-free aqueous system, no movement between leaflets need be considered. Loading must involve molecular changes yet to be described.

Another important aspect of substrate binding revealed by these studies is that endozepine added directly to mitoplasts (i.e., mitochondria from which the outer membrane has been removed) also increases the spectral shift associated with binding of cholesterol by P-450$_{scc}$. Evidently, no molecules from the outer membrane are necessary for this effect of endozepine. Clearly, it is not necessary for the endozepine receptor located in the outer mitochondrial membrane (10) to accompany endozepine into the inner membrane for this response to occur. When endozepine in nanomolar concentrations is added to homogeneous P-450$_{scc}$ with its electron carriers adrenodoxin reductase and adrenodoxin, NADPH and substrate cholesterol, the rate of side-chain cleavage (i.e., production of pregnenolone) is greatly accelerated compared with that seen without endozepine. This action of the peptide is likely a consequence of the increased affinity of the enzyme for its substrate demonstrated by the spectral shift described in the text above. Moreover, the acceleration of side-chain cleavage activity may be sufficient to account for the increased production of pregnenolone seen when endozepine is added to intact mitochondria—a response that formed the basis of the assay used to isolate endozepine. This response in turn is responsible for the steroidogenic stimulation produced by endozepine in the intact cell. It also is worthy of note that the effect of endozepine on the pure enzyme does not require an intact mitochondrial membrane or any membrane protein apart from the electron carriers.

We set out to detect specific binding of endozepine to adrenal mitochondria for the following reasons: endozepine was isolated from synaptosomes by inhibition of the binding of analogues of benzodiazepine, and reports indicated that outer mitochondrial membranes of adrenal cells show a high density of receptors for such analogues. For this purpose endozepine was iodinated with [125I] under gentle conditions that preserved full biological activity. In numerous studies no specific binding was observed with mitochondria from either Y-1 or bovine fasciculata cells.

We recently isolated endozepine from other steroidogenic cells including Y-1 mouse adrenal tumor cells, MA-10 Leydig cells and normal bovine Leydig cells. In the two cell lines MA-10 and Y-1, endozepine is synthesized de novo in the cells. Finally, the original form in which endozepine was isolated was des-(gly-ile)-endozepine (i.e., without the first two amino acids). We have since found that the full molecule (86 amino acids) is present in the bovine adrenal, and that both forms (86 and 84 amino acids) are present in MA-10 cells. Evidently, proteolytic cleavage of the peptide occurs either in the cell or during isolation.

References

1. Bar-Ami S, Fares F, Gavish M. Effect of hypophysectomy and hormone treatment on the induction of peripheral-type benzodiazepine binding sites in female rat genital axis. *Horm Metab Res* 1989;21:106–107.
2. Ong J, Kerr D. GABA-receptors in peripheral tissues. *Life Sci* 1990;46:1489–1501.
3. Hall PF. ACTH and corticosteroidogenesis. *Hormonal proteins and peptides,* vol XIII. New York: Academic Press, 1987;89–125.
4. Ohno Y, Yanagibashi K, Yonezawa Y, et al. A possible role of "steroidogenic factor" in the response to ACTH. *Endocrinol Jpn* 1983;30:335–343.
5. Privale CT, Crivello JF, Jefcoate CR. Regulation of intramitochondrial transfer of cholesterol. *Proc Natl Acad Sci USA* 1983;80:702–706.
6. Yanagibashi K, Ohno Y, Kawamura M, et al. The regulation of intracellular transport of cholesterol in bovine adrenal cells. Purification of a novel protein. *Endocrinology* 1988;123:2075–2082.
7. Besman MJ, Yanagibashi K, Lee TD, et al. Identification of des-(Gly-ile)-endozepine as an effector of corticotropin-dependent adrenal steroidogenesis: stimulation of cholesterol delivery is mediated by the peripheral benzodiazepine receptor. *Proc Natl Acad Sci USA* 1989;86:4897–4981.
8. Remmer H, Schenkman J, Estabrook RW, et al. Spectrophotometric responses of cytochrome P-450 to addition of various substrates. *Mol Pharmacol* 1966;2:187–196.
9. Kimura T. ACTH stimulation of cholesterol side-chain cleavage. *Mol Cell Biochem* 1981;36:105–122.
10. Anholt RRH, Pedersen PL, De Souza EP, et al. The peripheral type benzodiazepine receptor on outer mitochondrial membrane. *J Biol Chem* 1986;261:576–583.

Steroid Synthesis by Glial Cells

V. Papadopoulos, Ph.D., P. Guarneri, Ph.D., B. Pan, M.D., K.E. Krueger, Ph.D., and E. Costa, M.D.

Department of Anatomy and Cell Biology, Fidia-Georgetown Institute for the Neurosciences, Georgetown University School of Medicine, Washington, D.C. 20007

The presence of mitochondrial benzodiazepine receptors (MBRs) and of the cytochrome P-450 side-chain cleavage enzyme (P-450$_{scc}$) in glial cell cultures (1,2) suggests that these cells are steroidogenic. The steroids produced by glial cells are termed neurosteroids because they are believed to be targeted exclusively to brain cells. Moreover, some of the receptors for these steroids are not intracellular but are located on a class of receptors specific for the neurotransmitter γ-aminobutyric acid (GABA$_A$ receptors) (3,4). With particular relevance to these observations, other studies have shown that steroids such as pregnenolone sulfate and A-ring reduced metabolites of progesterone (3α-hydroxy-5α-pregnane-20-one and 5α-pregnane-3α,21-diol-20-one) appear to act on high-affinity recognition sites located on the transmembrane domain of the GABA$_A$ receptor modulating its responsiveness to the endogenous ligand (3–5).

Glial Cell Mitochondrial Steroid Biosynthesis

Steroid biosynthesis begins with the transport of the substrate cholesterol from various intracellular pools to the specific locations in the inner membrane where the P-450$_{scc}$ and other enzymes metabolize cholesterol into pregnenolone, the parent compound of every steroid (6).

Using antibodies specific for P-450$_{scc}$, we confirmed the presence of a comparable amount of the P-450$_{scc}$ enzyme in primary astroglial cells in culture and in the C6 glioma cell line (2). To examine the activity of the P-450$_{scc}$ present in C6 cells, hydroxylated analogues of cholesterol were

165

Table 1. Stimulation of glial cell mitochondrial pregnenolone formation by MBR ligands

	Pregnenolone (ng/mg protein)
Control	5.5 ± 0.7
PK-11195 (10^{-7} M)	10 ± 1.3
Ro5–4864 (10^{-7} M)	9.8 ± 1.1
Clonazepam (10^{-7} M)	5.7 ± 0.8
DBI (10^{-7} M)	14 ± 1.4
TTN (10^{-7} M)	12 ± 1.9
ODN (10^{-7} M)	5.8 ± 0.6

C6 glial cell mitochondria were prepared as previously described (10) and resuspended at a concentration of 2 mg protein per ml in buffer A (10 mM potassium phosphate buffer [pH 7], 0.25 M sucrose, 5 mM $MgCl_2$, 20 mM KCl, 15 mM triethanolamine-HCl) containing 5 μM trilostane. Samples to be tested were added in buffer A. Mixture was preincubated for 5 min at 37°C, and reaction was started by addition of 15 mM malate and 0.5 mM NADP. Incubation was continued for 15 min at 37°C. Pregnenolone formed was extracted and determined by radioimmunoassay. Data shown are means ±SD (n = 3) from a representative experiment. DBI, diazepam binding inhibitor; ODN, octadecaneuropeptide (DBI_{33-50}); TTN, triacontadecaneuropeptide (DBI_{17-50}).

used, which freely cross the mitochondrial membranes, thus accessing the $P-450_{scc}$ in the inner membrane. Three different hydroxylated cholesterols (25-, 22-, and 20-OH-cholesterol) stimulated mitochondrial production of pregnenolone by three- to fivefold. Notably, the glial cell $P-450_{scc}$ activity was found to be 10 times lower than the adrenocortical and testicular Leydig cell activity. Glial cell $P-450_{scc}$ activity also was tested with hydroxylated cholesterol analogues in the presence of aminoglutethimide, an inhibitor of adrenal, testis and ovarian $P-450_{scc}$. Aminoglutethimide inhibited in a concentration-dependent manner the pregnenolone formation from 25- and 22-OH-cholesterol, but failed to affect the conversion of 20-OH-cholesterol into pregnenolone. These findings suggest a functional analogy between adrenal and glial $P-450_{scc}$.

Role of Mitochondrial Benzodiazepine Receptors in Glial Cell Steroidogenesis

Benzodiazepines bind to $GABA_A$ receptors and to another class of receptors located in the outer mitochondrial membranes (MBRs). This class of receptors is functionally linked to adrenocortical and testicular Leydig cell steroid biosynthesis (7–9). MBRs are extremely abundant in

Table 2. Stimulation of glial cell steroid biosynthesis by Ro5–4864

	Cholesterol (cpm/mg protein)	Pregnenolone (cpm/mg protein)
Control	1255	825
Ro5–4864 (10^{-7} M)	1780	1697

C6 glial cells were washed with phosphate-buffered saline and incubated with lovastatin (20 µM) for 60 min. Trilostane (25 µM) and SU-10603 (10 µM) then were added and incubation continued for 30 min. Ro5–4864 was added to the culture dishes 15 min before the end of incubation. The reaction then was started by addition of [^{3}H]mevalonolactone (7 µCi/5 ml/100-mm dish) and cold mevalonolactone (20 µM). After 20 sec incubation time the reaction was stopped, steroids were extracted from both cells and media and separated through a silica sep-pak cartridge followed by a silica SiO$_6$ high-performance liquid chromatography column. Results shown are from a representative experiment.

steroid-producing cells, and their ligands can stimulate mitochondrial pregnenolone formation (7–9). This stimulation is due to increased intramitochondrial cholesterol transport, thereby increasing the substrate availability to the cytochrome P-450$_{scc}$ enzyme (10).

As found in peripheral steroidogenic tissues, mitochondria from primary glial cultures of neonatal rat cerebral cortex and from C6 glioma cells exhibit a high density of MBRs (2). We investigated whether MBR ligands affect pregnenolone formation in glial cell mitochondria. At nanomolar concentrations, PK-11195 and Ro5–4864 induced a twofold stimulation of mitochondrial steroid production (Table 1). A similar increase was obtained with anxiolytic benzodiazepines that bind to both classes of benzodiazepine recognition sites. However, clonazepam, a ligand selective for GABA$_A$ receptors, was ineffective at all concentrations tested. In these studies, exogenous cholesterol was not supplied to the mitochondria, which suggests that MBRs facilitate the transport of cholesterol from the outer mitochondrial membrane to the inner membrane, which then is metabolized by P-450$_{scc}$ to form pregnenolone.

Biosynthesis of [^{3}H]cholesterol and [^{3}H]pregnenolone was demonstrated in C6 glial cell cultures to occur within seconds on addition of the precursor [^{3}H]mevalonolactone. These experiments were performed in the presence of lovastatin (an inhibitor of 3β-hydroxy-3β-methylglutaryl-coenzyme A reductase), trilostane (an inhibitor of 3β-hydroxysteroid dehydrogenase) and SU-10603 (an inhibitor of 17α-hydroxylase). As indicated in Table 2, addition of 100 nM Ro5–4864 resulted in 141% and

Table 3. Antagonism of Ro5–4864–stimulated glial cell mitochondrial steroid biosynthesis by DBI

	Pregnenolone (ng/mg protein)	Percent increase
Control	4.4 ± 0.3	100
Ro5–4864 (10^{-7} M)	9.7 ± 0.8	227
DBI (10^{-5} M)	6.6 ± 0.4	100
DBI (10^{-5} M) + Ro5–4864 (10^{-7} M)	8.6 ± 0.5	130

C6 glial cell mitochondria were prepared and incubated with the indicated compounds, as described in Table 1. Pregnenolone was measured by radioimmunoassay. Data shown are means $\pm$ SD (n = 3) from a representative experiment.

205% increases in cholesterol and pregnenolone formation, respectively. These data demonstrate that MBR ligands also stimulate steroid formation in cultured glial cells.

Role of Diazepam Binding Inhibitor and its Processing Products in Glial Cell Mitochondrial Pregnenolone Formation

In addition to synthetic ligands, we examined whether endogenous ligands for MBRs known to be in glial cells can stimulate glial cell steroidogenesis. A putative endogenous ligand for MBRs is the polypeptide diazepam binding inhibitor (DBI) (11), previously shown to displace drugs from MBRs, and to be highly expressed in steroidogenic cells (12,13). DBI also was found in C6 glioma cell extracts. Furthermore, nanomolar concentrations of DBI stimulated pregnenolone formation by 2.5-fold in mitochondrial fractions from C6 glioma cells (Table 1). These results agree with our previous findings that DBI potently stimulates adrenocortical and Leydig cell mitochondrial steroidogenesis, essentially via its interaction with MBRs (13,14).

Numerous studies have demonstrated that DBI can be processed to different peptide fragments in cells (15,16). Two of these fragments are of particular interest: an octadecaneuropeptide (ODN; DBI_{33-50}) which, given intraventricularly to rats, elicits a proconflict response due to stimulation of $GABA_A$ receptors; and a triacontadecaneuropeptide (TTN; DBI_{17-50}) that also causes proconflict effects due to a selective stimulation of MBRs (16). TTN, at nanomolar concentrations, stimulated C6 glioma mitochondrial pregnenolone formation by 2.3-fold, whereas ODN was completely ineffective at all concentrations tested (Table 1).

DBI as a Partial Agonist of MBRs

Data presented in Tables 1 and 3 indicate that DBI stimulates pregnenolone formation by glial cell mitochondria. Notably, high concentrations of DBI (10 µM) gave a lower stimulation of steroid synthesis than 100 nM DBI (compare Tables 1 and 3). When DBI was added in combination with a maximally stimulating concentration of Ro5–4864 (100 nM), the stimulatory effect of Ro5–4864 was abolished. These data indicate that in C6 glial cells, DBI may act as a partial agonist of MBRs.

Conclusions

Our data demonstrate that primary glial cells and C6 glioma cells express a functional P-450$_{scc}$. C6 mitochondrial preparations have been used to show that MBR ligands and DBI or TTN stimulate pregnenolone formation, the precursor of progesterone and other bioactive steroid metabolites in the CNS. DBI also has been demonstrated to be a partial agonist of MBRs. These glial cell and mitochondrial models provide useful systems for examining the bioactivity of drugs specific for MBRs, in relation to their effects on neurosteroidogenesis. Because steroids affect a number of neuronal activities, release of neurosteroids produced by glia may have a major impact on neuronal cell function, and thus may be a fundamental mechanism in the regulation of brain function.

References

1. Baulieu E-E, Robel P. Neurosteroids: a new brain function? *J Steroid Biochem Mol Biol* 1990;37:395–403.
2. Papadopoulos V, Guarneri P, Krueger KE, et al. Pregnenolone biosynthesis in C6 glioma cell mitochondria: regulation by endogenous diazepam binding inhibitor via mitochondrial benzodiazepine receptors. Submitted.
3. Majewska MD, Harrison NL, Schwartz RD, et al. Steroid hormone metabolites are barbiturate-like modulators of the GABA receptor. *Science* 1986;232:1004–1007.
4. Puia G, Santi MR, Vicini S, et al. Neurosteroids act on recombinant human GABA$_A$ receptors. *Neuron* 1990;4:759–765.
5. Purdy RH, Morrow AL, Moore PH, et al. Stress-induced elevations of γ-aminobutyric acid type A receptor-active steroids in the rat brain. *Proc Natl Acad Sci USA* 1991; 88:4553–4557.
6. Hall PF. Cellular organization for steroidogenesis. *Int Rev Cytol* 1984;86:53–95.
7. Mukhin AG, Papadopoulos V, Costa E, et al. Mitochondrial benzodiazepine receptors regulate steroid biosynthesis. *Proc Natl Acad Sci USA* 1989;86:9813–9816.

8. Papadopoulos V, Mukhin AG, Costa E, et al. The peripheral-type benzodiazepine receptor is functionally linked to Leydig cell steroidogenesis. *J Biol Chem* 1990;265:3772–3779.

9. Papadopoulos V, Nowzari FB, Krueger KE. Hormone-stimulated steroidogenesis is coupled to mitochondrial benzodiazepine receptors. *J Biol Chem* 1991;266:3682–3687.

10. Krueger KE, Papadopoulos V. Peripheral-type benzodiazepine receptors mediate translocation of cholesterol from outer to inner mitochondrial membranes in adrenocortical cells. *J Biol Chem* 1990;265:15015–15022.

11. Guidotti A, Forchetti CM, Corda MG, et al. Isolation, characterization, and purification to homogeneity of an endogenous polypeptide with agonistic action on BDZ receptors. *Proc Natl Acad Sci USA* 1983;80:3531–3533.

12. Bovolin P, Schlichting J, Miyata J, et al. Distribution and characterization of diazepam binding inhibitor (DBI) in peripheral tissues of rat. *Regul Pept* 1990;29:267–281.

13. Gray PW, Glaister D, Seeburg PH, et al. Cloning and expression of a cDNA for human benzodiazepam binding inhibitor, a natural ligand of an allosteric regulatory site of the γ-aminobutyric acid type A receptor. *Proc Natl Acad Sci USA* 1986;83:7547–7551.

14. Besman MJ, Yanagibashi K, Lee TD, et al. Identification of des-(Gly-Ile)-endozepine as an effector of corticotropin-dependent adrenal steroidogenesis: stimulation of cholesterol delivery is mediated by the peripheral benzodiazepine receptor. *Proc Natl Acad Sci USA* 1989;86:4897–4901.

15. Slobodyansky E, Guidotti A, Wambebe C, et al. Isolation and characterization of a rat brain triakontatetraneuropeptide, a posttranslational product of diazepam binding inhibitor: specific action at the Ro5–4864 recognition site. *J Neurochem* 1989;53:1276–1284.

16. Costa E, Guidotti A. Diazepam Binding Inhibitor (DBI): a peptide with multiple biological actions. *Life Sci* 1991;49:325–344.

Is There a Pharmacology of Brain Steroidogenesis?

E. Costa, M.D., E. Romeo, M.D., J. Auta, V. Papadopoulos, Ph.D.,
*A. Kozikowski, Ph.D., and A. Guidotti, M.D.

Fidia-Georgetown Institute for the Neurosciences, Georgetown University School
of Medicine, Washington, D.C.; and *Mayo Clinic,
Jacksonville, Florida 32224

The pioneering work of E.-E. Baulieu and colleagues has provided several lines of evidence supporting the view that the brain can synthesize steroids (1). These investigators also showed that glial cells are probably the most important steroidogenic cells in the brain (2). Preliminary evidence indicates that glial cells produce pregnenolone sulfate, dehydroepiandrosterone sulfate, 3α-hydroxy-5α-pregnan-20-one (3α-OH-DHP) and 3α-21-dihydroxy-5α-pregnan-20-one (THDOC). These steroids can bind with high affinity to sites probably located on the transmembrane domain of the heterooligomeric integral membrane protein functioning as a γ-aminobutyric acid(GABA)$_A$ receptor, and thereby modulate receptor responsiveness to GABA (3). Because these steroids have as a target a neuronal structure functioning in neuron to neuron signaling, they have been termed neurosteroids. The term helps differentiate this mechanism of regulation from that of steroids binding to specific fluid receptors which form a steroid receptor complex that translocates to the nucleus to regulate gene expression. Neurosteroid precursors are synthesized in mitochondria under the regulation of a recognition site for benzodiazepines located in the outer membrane (mitochondrial benzodiazepine receptor, MBR), which has been cloned and contains a consensus for the action of protein kinase A (4). MBRs belong to a class of nonneuronal receptors termed peripheral benzodiazepine receptors (PBRs), which also includes receptors located on the

Table 1. Binding specificity, action on GABA$_A$ receptors and stimulation of pregnenolone formation by MBR ligands

Drug	MBR [³H]-4'Cl-Diazepam (rat glial cells) K_i;nM	GABA$_A$ Receptors [³H]Flumazenil (rat cerebellum) K_i;nM	Modulation of GABA-operated Cl⁻ channel* Flumazenil Sensitive	Flumazenil Insensitive	Pregnenolone formation from mitochondria of C₆-2B glioma cells EC₅₀(nM)	Maximum increase (% of control)
FGIN-1-27§	4.4 ± 0.95	>1000	No	No	3.3	200
Alpidem	0.5 ± 0.032	28 ± 2.2	Yes (+)	No	1.0	200
4'Cl-Diazepam	1.0 ± 0.025	>1000	No	Yes (−)	10	175
PK-11195	1.2 ± 0.050	>1000	No	No	10	108
Diazepam	80 ± 10	20 ± 1.8	Yes (+)	No	750†	50†
Zolpidem	>1000	40 ± 0.92	Yes (+)	No	800†	20†

*Data from refs. 3 and 7.

†Data obtained in Y1 adrenal cortical cells. For details see ref. 8.

(+) = Positive modulation

(−) = Negative modulation

§FGIN-1-27

membranes of circulating mononuclear cells, macrophages and thymocytes (5). Ligands for PBRs display immunomodulatory activity such as the enhancement of chemotaxis and release of interleukins (5).

Several classes of benzodiazepines exist: those that bind exclusively to $GABA_A$ receptors (i.e., zolpidem), those that bind selectively to $GABA_A$ receptors but also bind to MBRs (i.e., diazepam), those that bind with high affinity to MBRs but also bind with relatively high affinity to $GABA_A$ receptors (i.e., alpidem), those that bind to MBRs selectively but can inhibit the action of GABA on $GABA_A$ receptors by acting on a site resistant to flumazenil inhibition (i.e., 4'Cl-diazepam), and those that bind exclusively to MBRs and exert their action on $GABA_A$ receptors via an activation of glial cell steroidogenesis (i.e., FGIN-1–27).

The pharmacological properties of these various classes of compounds are characterized by the data in Table 1. This table shows that alpidem has the highest affinity for MBRs, with a high intrinsic efficacy (it doubles the rate of pregnenolone synthesis in isolated mitochondria). Diazepam also has a high affinity for MBRs, albeit smaller than that for $GABA_A$ receptors, but has a low efficacy on steroidogenesis. Hence, one can infer that whereas diazepam can elicit an anxiolytic action mediated via $GABA_A$ receptors, without a concomitant activation of neurosteroid production, alpidem given at pharmacological doses elicits both actions. In contrast, zolpidem in pharmacological doses elicits a selective action on $GABA_A$ receptors, virtually without activation of neurosteroid biosynthesis. 4'Cl-diazepam has a selective action on steroidogenesis over a broad range of doses, but at high doses causes convulsions because it inhibits GABA action on $GABA_A$ receptors (6). FGIN-1–27 has an exclusive action on MBRs, with an efficacy and affinity close to that of 4'Cl-diazepam and alpidem. But unlike 4'Cl-diazepam and alpidem, FGIN-1–27 does not have a direct action on $GABA_A$ receptors.

FGIN-1–27 acts as an agonist at MBRs, over a wide range of doses. FGIN-1–27 is the prototype of a series of 2-aryl-3-indoleacetamide derivatives that displace 4'Cl-diazepam from primary cultures of rat cerebellar glial cells (Table 1). The displacing potency of FGIN-1–27 is significantly higher than that of zolpidem and diazepam, but close to that of alpidem. However, unlike diazepam, zolpidem and alpidem, this new compound fails to displace flumazenil from the benzodiazepine modulatory sites of $GABA_A$ receptors (Table 1). Moreover, FGIN-1–27 fails to displace [^{3}H]zolpidem or [^{35}S]-t-butyl-bicyclophosphorothionate binding, and does not modify in a positive or negative manner the binding of GABA to its own recognition sites. FGIN-1–27 at doses of 10^{-6} M or higher fails to displace [3H]baclofen from $GABA_B$ receptors of rat brain membranes; [3H]spiperone from dopamine or serotonin (5HT) receptors; [3H]-ketanserine from $5HT_2$ receptors; [3H]glycine, [3H]MK801 or [3H]AMPA from glutamate receptors; [3H]naloxone or [3H]PPP from opiate and sigma receptors; [3H]-L-365, 260 from cholecystokinin receptors; and [125I]pindolol from β-adrenergic receptors. Moreover, FGIN-1–27 stimulates pregnenolone formation from glial cell mitochondria, with a potency and efficacy comparable to that of alpidem (Table 1).

The experiments reported in Table 2 were conducted to determine whether a correlation exists among MBR binding selectivity, the ability to synthesize neurosteroids, and anticonvulsant activity in rats. To this end, the effect of FGIN-1–27 (a selective steroidogenic ligand of MBRs) was compared with the effect of the steroid THDOC (a potent, flumazenil-resistant, positive modulator of GABA efficacy on $GABA_A$ receptors), diazepam and alpidem (two drugs acting as positive modulators of $GABA_A$ receptors and as steroidogenic MBR ligands), PK-11195 (a selective steroidogenic MBR ligand of limited efficacy) and muscimol (a high-affinity $GABA_A$ receptor agonist) on their ability to reduce isoniazid- or bicuculline-induced seizures. Table 2 indicates that all the compounds tested (except PK-11195) prolong the onset of isoniazid convulsions. Isoniazid inhibits GABA synthesis, thereby reducing brain GABA stores. Moreover, THDOC and FGIN-1–27, even given in sedative and ataxic doses, failed to delay the onset of bicuculline-induced seizures. PK-11195

Table 2. Protection by MBR ligands, THDOC and muscimol on isoniazid- and bicuculline-induced seizures in rats

Drug (mg/kg i.v.)	Isoniazid	Bicuculline
	(onset of generalized tonic-clonic seizures/min)	
Vehicle	40 ± 5.7 (9)	2.5 ± 0.012 (6)
FGIN-1–27 (2.5)	60* ± 3.2 (6)	2.3 ± 0.018 (6)
THDOC (5)	62* ± 4.0 (5)	2.8 ± 0.020 (5)
Diazepam (0.5)	55* ± 2.5 (5)	5.9* ± 0.047 (5)
Diazepam (1)	84* ± 6.4 (5)	8.0* ± 0.090 (5)
Alpidem (5)	87* ± 4.9 (5)	5.8* ± 0.080 (5)
PK-11195 (10)	51 ± 7.1 (5)	2.7 ± 0.58 (5)
Muscimol (4)	64* ± 3.1 (5)	4.5* ± 0.57 (5)

Isoniazid (400 mg/kg s.c.) was injected 30 min before drug administration. Bicuculline was infused intravenously (i.v.) at a rate of 124 nmol/min. Perfusion with bicuculline was initiated 10 min after drug administration. *$p<0.05$ compared to vehicle-treated rats.

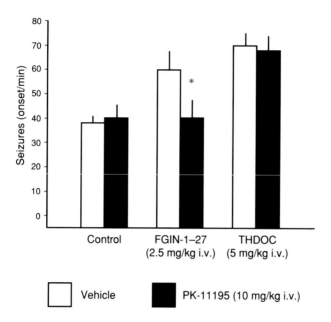

Figure 1. PK-11195 blocks FGIN-1–27 but not THDOC antagonism of isoniazid-induced seizures. *p<0.05.

also fails to delay bicuculline convulsions. Thus, the pharmacological profile of FGIN-1–27 and THDOC contrasts that of diazepam, alpidem and muscimol, which, by virtue of their direct action at the GABA$_A$ receptor allosteric or isoteric sites, protect from both isoniazid- and bicuculline-induced seizures.

We previously reported (3) that THDOC in nM concentrations facilitates GABA action, and in μM concentrations can elicit Cl⁻ currents that are antagonized by bicuculline. This finding suggests that THDOC can directly activate the GABA$_A$ receptor complex but, by this mechanism, it cannot overcome bicuculline blockade of GABA$_A$ receptors (3). In line with these findings, the data in Table 2 show that THDOC cannot overcome the bicuculline convulsions that are readily antagonized by drugs that act on the recognition site for benzodiazepines located on the GABA$_A$ receptor, or by GABA$_A$ receptor agonists that can displace bicuculline and overcome its effects. Because FGIN-1–27 acts similarly to THDOC, one can surmise that the action of this compound ultimately depends on its ability to stimulate steroidogenesis in glial cells. In support of this contention, the data in Figure 1 show that the action of PK-11195—a selective, high-affinity, low-efficacy ligand for MBRs—differs from that of FGIN-1–27. This difference may be because, due to its partial agonistic activity (Table 1), PK-11195 blocks the action of FGIN-1–27. In animals treated with PK-11195, the action of FGIN-1–27 on isoniazid convulsions is obliterated, whereas the action of THDOC persists despite the pretreatment.

References

1. Baulieu E-E, Robel PJ. Neurosteroids: a new brain function? *J Steroid Biochem Mol Biol* 1990;37:395–403.
2. Jung-Testas I, Hu ZY, Baulieu E-E, et al. Neurosteroids: biosynthesis of pregnenolone and progesterone in primary cultures of rat glial cells. *Endocrinology* 1989;125:2083–2091.
3. Puia G, Santi MR, Vicini S, et al. Neurosteroids act on recombinant human GABA$_A$ receptors. *Neuron* 1990;4:759–765.
4. Sprengel R, Werner P, Seeburg PH, et al. Molecular cloning and expression of cDNA encoding a peripheral-type benzodiazepine receptor. *J Biol Chem* 1989;264:20415–20421.
5. Taupin V, Herbelin A, Descamps-Latscha B, et al. Endogenous anxiogenic peptide, ODN-diazepam-binding inhibitor, and benzodiazepines enhance the production of interleukins-1 and tumor necrosis factor by human monocytes. *Lymphokine Cytokine Res* 1991;10:7–13.
6. Puia G, Santi MR, Vicini S, et al. Differences in the negative allosteric modulation of γ-aminobutyric acid receptors elicited by 4'Cl-diazepam and by β-carboline-3-carboxylate ester: a study with natural and reconstituted receptors. *Proc Natl Acad Sci USA* 1989;86:7275–7279.
7. Puia G, Vicini S, Seeburg PH, et al. Influence of recombinant gamma-aminobutyric acid-A receptor subunit composition on the action of allosteric modulators of gamma-aminobutyric acid-gated Cl⁻ currents. *Mol Pharmacol* 1991;39:691–696.
8. Krueger KE, Papadopoulos V. Peripheral-type benzodiazepine receptors mediate translocation of cholesterol from outer to inner mitochondrial membranes in adrenocortical cells. *J Biol Chem* 1990;265:15015–15022.

Subject Index

177